Integrated Assessment
An Assessment Alternative

McDougal Littell

THE LANGUAGE OF
LITERATURE

AMERICAN LITERATURE

McDougal Littell
A HOUGHTON MIFFLIN COMPANY
Evanston, Illinois ◆ Boston ◆ Dallas

Acknowledgments

"They're Made Out of Meat" by Terry Bisson. Copyright © 1991 by Terry Bisson. Originally published in OMNI magazine, April 1991. Reprinted by permission of the author's agent, Susan Ann Protter. All rights reserved.

"Suzie Wong Doesn't Live Here" by Diane Mei Lin Mark. Reprinted by permission of the author.

"A Blizzard Under Blue Sky," from *Cowboys Are My Weakness* by Pam Houston. Copyright © 1992 by Pam Houston. Reprinted by permission of W. W. Norton & Company, Inc.

"Advice to Youth" and "Foreign Critics" by Mark Twain, from *The Complete Essays of Mark Twain*, edited by Charles Neider. Copyright © 1963 by Charles Neider. Reprinted by permission of HarperCollins Publishers, Inc.

"Working Girls," from *Chicago Poems* by Carl Sandburg. Copyright © 1916 by Holt, Rinehart and Winston, renewed 1944 by Carl Sandburg. Reprinted by permission of Harcourt Brace & company.

"What Work Is," from *What Work Is* by Philip Levine. Copyright © 1991 by Philip Levine. Reprinted by permission of Alfred A. Knopf, Inc.

"Whatever Happened to Spare Time?" by Michael Posner, from the *World Press Review*, September 1991. Reprinted courtesy of *World Press Review*, New York and the *Globe and Mail*, Toronto.

"The Lesson" by Harry Mark Petrakis. Copyright © 1998 by Harry Mark Petrakis. Reprinted by permission of the author.

Contents

General Information for the Teacher

WHY INTEGRATED ASSESSMENT?

Since the publication of *Becoming a Nation of Readers* in 1985, educational reform efforts have focused on creating classroom practices that foster "lifelong readers." To this end, teachers at all levels have worked to develop meaningful reading and writing activities for the classroom—"authentic literacy tasks"—that mirror the kinds of activities that students find in the larger world outside the classroom. Such tasks include making sense of a piece of writing and communicating that understanding to others.

While teachers and textbooks have made great strides in introducing integrated, purposeful activities into the classroom, similar innovations in reading assessment have lagged behind—until now.

Connection to National and State Frameworks and Tests

McDougal Littell's pedagogy in *The Language of Literature* program, including this integrated assessment component, is closely allied with the most recent federal and state curriculum frameworks and assessment initiatives, including

- the National Assessment of Educational Progress (NAEP), which reports student progress at a state-by-state as well as at a national level
- the New Standards Project
- the English Language Arts Standards of the National Council of Teachers of English (NCTE) and the International Reading Association (IRA)
- new frameworks and assessments developed or being developed by state education departments across the country

These initiatives have sought to bridge the gap between the thoughtful reading, writing, and discussion activities students now engage in during class time and the tests they take to demonstrate what they have learned.

In developing this integrated assessment package, McDougal Littell has benefited from consultation with NAEP authors, NCTE professionals, state education coordinators, and classroom teachers who have been active in creating new types of reading and writing assessments for their states and districts. Because of this professional consensus on reading, writing, and assessment, McDougal Littell's integrated assessments are particularly helpful in preparing students for federal and statewide (as well as many district-wide) assessments.

Emphasis on Authenticity

The most important aspect of integrated assessment is the emphasis on the authenticity of the tasks students are asked to perform. To be thought-provoking and purposeful from the students' perspective, these tasks need to resemble meaningful reading and writing experiences that students are likely to encounter in the real world. For example, learners in the real world would likely discuss a story, an article, or a book they have read; then they might share their reactions (or promote their ideas) in a written analysis or a review. They would rarely encounter a multiple-choice test on their reading—except, of course, in an academic environment, and then only if they were students.

Currently, thoughtful discussions and authentic reading and writing take place in classrooms all the time. Students are now encouraged to develop their ideas and think through their reasoning; they have many opportunities to interpret a selection and then to reflect on and refine their interpretations. This kind of elaborated thinking is the focus of McDougal Littell's integrated assessment. Conventional assessments have often failed to adequately measure what students know and think, because multiple-choice tests leave no room for the elaboration of students' ideas. Integrated assessment, on the other hand, creates an authentic literacy experience. It requires students not only to comprehend what they have read but also to think about it and communicate their ideas to others.

What Integrated Assessment Can Do for You and Your Students

Because the authentic tasks in McDougal Littell's integrated assessment look very much like those in the student book, students can demonstrate what they *have* learned rather than reveal what they have not learned. The message to students is clear: tests become a continuation of classroom activities rather than separate entities that require special test-taking skills.

When used in combination with the formal assessment materials offered in the program, the integrated assessment can tell you not only what students comprehend from what they've read but also how well they can apply the skills and strategies they have acquired. You'll be able to monitor both the accumulation of students' knowledge and the development of their critical thinking skills.

When used alone, the integrated assessment is useful in showing you the range of student abilities—not only in reading and writing, but in speaking and listening as well. Because the assessment also includes multimodal activities, it can help you identify the different learning styles of your students so that you can better address their individual needs. Integrated assessment is also useful as a diagnostic tool for you to identify specific areas where a student may be having trouble, such as in analytical thinking, for example, or in articulating and communicating ideas.

Finally, because this package was developed in accordance with federal and state guidelines, McDougal Littell's integrated assessment will prepare students for taking individual state assessments that are currently in use or under development.

WHAT DOES INTEGRATED ASSESSMENT TEST?

Conventional multiple-choice tests do not focus on the amount of thoughtful reasoning that goes into answering a test item. However, integrated assessments do. They focus both on what students understand and on how students reason. The assessments in this package require students to record their thoughts and to write about what they understand at several stages in the process of reading and interpretation. As such, the assessments are designed to test a variety of skills over a period of time. The following chart shows the general and specific skills that each assessment addresses.

General Skills and Abilities

- Depth and sophistication of reading comprehension
- Process and development of thinking
- Facility with written and oral language
- Ability to work cooperatively and learn from others
- Ability to work independently and stay on task
- Ability to respond to a writing prompt in a specified period of time

---

Specific Skills and Abilities

- Response-based and critical reading strategies taught in the program
- Speaking and listening skills practiced in the program
- Writing skills taught in each unit
- Editing and proofreading skills taught in the program

CONTENTS OF McDOUGAL LITTELL'S INTEGRATED ASSESSMENT

This integrated assessment package for *The Language of Literature* includes copymasters for seven unit integrated assessments and one end-of-year integrated assessment. Each unit assessment includes a reading selection and six pages of test activities. Students read the selection and write their responses in the spaces provided on the test. The end-of-year assessment consists of three selections contained in a Reader plus a Student Response Booklet for students to write in.

Following is a summary of each section of the integrated assessments and suggestions for classroom management.

Instructions Page

The first page of each assessment tells students what the test consists of and on what criteria their reading, writing, and speaking and listening will be evaluated.

Suggestions Go over these instructions with students, especially the first few times you administer the tests, to make sure they know what they are expected to do. For the unit assessments, check to see that students have copies of the selections being tested. For the end-of-year assessment, make sure students have copies of the Reader and the Student Response Booklet.

Before You Read

Every assessment begins with a short prereading exercise to activate students' prior knowledge and get them thinking about a central theme or issue in the selection. This exercise usually takes the form of a graphic device designed to help students organize their ideas and direct their thinking to the activities that follow.

Reading and Responding

On every assessment, students are asked to respond to a selection while they are reading it. This reader-response activity requires students to jot down their thoughts and reactions as they read. Their comments will be similar in kind to those of the student readers featured in the Model for Active Reading starting on page 8 of the student book. For those students who may not be comfortable alternately reading and writing, there is another option in the unit assessments: they can stop at specified points in the selection and write their comments.

Suggestions Before administering the unit assessment, especially the first one or two, you might review with students the active reading strategies on page 7 of the student book as well as the readers' comments on the model. The Reader for the end-of-year assessment has space alongside the selections for students to write their responses.

Reading Selection(s)

The selection or selections that students are being tested on reflect the genre of the unit they have just completed. The selections(s) will be from 2 to 5 pages long. If a unit consists of short works (e.g., poems), there may be more than one selection in the unit assessment.

Reflecting and Rethinking

This section of the test is for students to reflect on their responses to the selection and to develop their own interpretations. Because this meaning-making is such a crucial stage in reading comprehension as well as in thinking, the unit assessment has two options. The first contains questions for written responses. The second is a multimodal activity—for example, drawing or working in pairs—for students who may have trouble composing their thoughts at this early stage. Both options in this section elicit a basic understanding of the selection, although through two different learning styles.

Suggestions For those students who choose the option to work in pairs, you might suggest that they move to a quiet corner of the room so that they do not disturb the other students. If you believe that having students work in pairs compromises the accuracy of scoring their reading performance, then have students complete Option Two on their own.

Sharing with Others

This section of the assessment always involves a small group of classmates. Its purpose is twofold: First, the group discussion forces students to go beyond their individual interpretations to consider other viewpoints. Second, the questions or activities broaden students' thinking to consider larger themes and implications and at times to make a comparison with another selection. This section of the assessment is also useful in preparing students for the writing assignments that follow.

Suggestions You may wish to assist students in forming their groups and monitor their discussions as you see fit.

Responding in Writing

Every assessment concludes with two writing prompts for students to choose between. For the unit assessment, you will have to give students clean paper to write on. The end-of-year assessment includes two ruled pages students can use to write their final drafts, but you will have to give them paper for their first drafts. Remind them to turn in these pages with their booklets.

Suggestions Make sure students understand what is expected for each writing option before they start this section. Wherever applicable for the unit assessments, the writing prompts reflect the writing activities that appear on the Writing Workshop pages for the unit being tested. Writing Workshops usually occur at the end of each of the two parts in a unit. Following each writing prompt is a box with standards to help students focus their writing and include the necessary information within the time period. These standards are modified from the Standards for Writing box that appears on the first page of the Writing Workshops.

If there are enough computers available for all students and all students know how to use them, permit students to use the computers for these extended written responses. Have dictionaries and thesauruses available and encourage students to use them.

Revising and Editing

Only the end-of-year assessment includes a revising and editing section. You may give students either of two options: 1) exchanging papers with a partner who will offer suggestions for revision; or 2) working alone to revise their own papers. To help students focus on the most important aspects of the paper to evaluate, an evaluation form tailored to each writing assignment is provided in the Student Response Booklet.

Finalizing and Proofreading

This section is also found only on the end-of-year assessment. Before students turn in their final drafts, they should mark corrections in grammar, usage, punctuation, and spelling. Encourage students to draw a line through incorrect words and to use proofreading marks. Count only students' uncorrected errors when evaluating their work.

HOW TO ADMINISTER THE INTEGRATED ASSESSMENTS
Preparation

For each student, you will need to copy, collate, and staple each of the following:
- 8–11 pages for each of the Unit Integrated Assessments (including the reading selection(s))
- 6 pages for the End-of-Year Reader
- 14 pages for the End-of-Year Student Response Booklet

You will also need to make enough copies of the Writing Assessment Forms (located in the answer key) to enable you to score the Responding in Writing section of each assessment.

Scheduling the Assessments

Each unit assessment is designed to be administered to students after they have finished studying a unit. You will need to set aside two class periods to administer the tests.

The unit assessment is intended to draw on material in the unit whenever possible. In most cases, the two writing prompts on each unit assessment match the writing modes taught in the Writing Workshops for that unit. (The exceptions are creative modes and reports, which are generally not used as assessment instruments.) In addition, in some of the assessments, students are asked in the Sharing with Others section to compare the assessment selection with a selection in the unit that they have read. Note, however, that both the writing prompts and the comparisons with other selections are general enough so that students do not have to read all the selections or complete both Writing Workshops in a unit in order to take the unit assessment.

It is possible to administer a unit assessment before students have finished the unit. For example, it may be used as a diagnostic tool in the middle of a unit. You may even choose to skip one of the assessments for a given unit.

Because the end-of-year assessment includes several selections for students to read and compare, it is an appropriate instrument for evaluating their accomplishments toward the end of the school year. Moreover, in length and format, it serves as excellent practice for students who must take similar state-administered assessments.

Timing the Assessments

Each unit assessment takes about two 45-minute time periods, or about 90 minutes. The end-of-year assessment covers about five 45-minute time periods. If you have block scheduling in your school, you may be able to administer the unit assessment in one time period.

The charts on the next page suggest the approximate amount of time to spend on each section of the unit and end-of-year assessments. However, all of these assessments are intended to be flexible enough to accommodate a variety of teaching styles and individual classroom schedules. Feel free to adapt the assessment to your particular needs. For example, you might want students to do a portion of the unit assessment (such as sections A and B or section E) at home to reduce the amount of class time spent on the test. On the other hand, you may want to spend a longer time on each section of the assessment so as to cover three time periods, or about 2 hours and 15 minutes, in all.

With the end-of-year assessment, you may find that Reading and Responding for some selections (particularly poetry) will not require 20 minutes. You may want to allow less time for this activity and more time for Reflecting and Rethinking or Sharing with Others.

Whatever you decide, be sure to tell students how long you expect them to spend on each section of the assessment. You may wish to keep a pacing chart on the board and update it periodically as you would for any timed test.

Unit Integrated Assessment

DAY ONE

A. Before You Read	about 5 minutes
B. Reading and Responding	about 30 minutes
C. Reflecting and Rethinking	about 10 minutes

DAY TWO

D. Sharing with Others	about 15 minutes
E. Responding in Writing	about 30 minutes

End-of-Year Integrated Assessment

DAY ONE: Section One

1A. Before You Read	about 10 minutes
1B. Reading and Responding	about 20 minutes
1C. Reflecting and Rethinking	about 15 minutes

DAY TWO: Section Two

2A. Reading and Responding	about 20 minutes
2B. Reflecting and Rethinking	about 10 minutes
2C. Sharing with Others	about 15 minutes

DAY THREE: Section Three

3A. Reading and Responding	about 20 minutes
3B. Reflecting and Rethinking	about 10 minutes
3C. Sharing with Others	about 15 minutes

DAY FOUR: Section Four

4A. Responding in Writing: First Draft	about 45 minutes

DAY FIVE: Section Five

5A. Revising and Editing	about 20 minutes
5B. Finalizing and Proofreading Your Draft	about 25 minutes

Scoring the Assessments

Sample responses for each question or activity can be found in the answer key for each assessment. For the writing prompts, rubrics are provided for weak, average, and strong writing. These rubrics—basically the same as the standards listed on the unit assessments—are modified from the Standards for Writing found on the first page of the Writing Workshops in the student book.

If you would like to assign a score for the reading and writing performance, a scoring guide for each is located at the back of this booklet. Keep in mind that these integrated assessments require holistic scoring and are flexible enough to accommodate a variety of uses. For example, if you believe that reading comprehension is more accurately assessed through solitary activities, then evaluate students' responses *before* section D of the unit assessment. (You can also require students who choose Option Two in section C to work alone instead of with a partner.) On the other hand, if you believe that reading comprehension is more authentically assessed through a combination of solitary and group activities, then evaluate all student responses on the assessment. Similarly, to keep the writing score for the end-of-year assessment tied to what students can do strictly on their own, you can choose to have them edit their own papers rather than work with peer reviewers.

Unit One: Integrated Assessment

Reading, Writing, Speaking and Listening

INSTRUCTIONS

You'll be spending about 90 minutes reading and responding to the selection "They're Made Out of Meat." At different times, you will be working alone, with a partner, and with a small group of classmates.

This booklet is the place for you to write down all your thoughts about the selection—your first impressions as well as other ideas you have as you continue to think about and discuss the selection. In evaluating this booklet, your teacher will look at all of your writing, so please respond as completely and as honestly as you can.

In evaluating your reading, your teacher will look at how well you

- connect ideas in the selection to your own experience and to selections in the unit
- understand the attitudes of the characters in the selection
- understand the themes in the selection

In evaluating your writing, your teacher will look at how well you

- state your main ideas
- give details and examples to support your ideas
- organize your thoughts

In evaluating your speaking and listening, your teacher will look at how well you

- contribute to group discussion
- listen to other group members
- stay on task during the group activity
- cooperate with other group members

A. BEFORE YOU READ

In Part Two of Unit One, you read about the first contact, centuries ago, between Native Americans and Europeans and between Africans and Europeans. You also read about modern first encounters between Americans and strangers they met while traveling in the United States and in Africa. From your reading and your own experiences, what can you say about how people tend to view others at first contact? List some attitudes on the lines in the diagram below.

Attitudes at first contact:

B. READING AND RESPONDING

Read the selection "They're Made Out of Meat." As you read, write down your thoughts and reactions in the box below. To help with your responses, use the active reading strategies: **question** what you read, **connect** the selection to your own life, **predict** what will happen, **clarify** earlier confusion, and **evaluate,** or make judgments about, the situations and characters.

If you'd prefer to divide the story into sections, follow these guidelines:

- Read until you get to the sentence on page 5, ending with ". . . And they've been trying to get in touch with us for almost a hundred of their years." Stop and write your response to what you've read so far.

- Start reading again and continue to the end of the story. Then write your response.

NOTES

They're Made Out of Meat

Terry Bisson

NOTES

"They're made out of meat."

"Meat?"

"Meat. They're made out of meat."

"Meat?"

"There's no doubt about it. We picked up several from different parts of the planet, took them aboard our recon vessels,[1] and probed them all the way through. They're completely meat."

"That's impossible. What about the radio signals? The messages to the stars?"

"They use the radio waves to talk, but the signals don't come from them. The signals come from machines."

"So who made the machines? That's who we want to contact."

"*They* made the machines. That's what I'm trying to tell you. Meat made the machines."

"That's ridiculous. How can meat make a machine? You're asking me to believe in sentient[2] meat."

"I'm not asking you. I'm telling you. These creatures are the only sentient race in that sector, and they're made out of meat."

"Maybe they're like the orfolei.[3] You know, a carbon-based intelligence that goes through a meat stage."

"Nope. They're born meat and they die meat. We studied them for several of their life spans, which didn't take long. Do you have any idea of the life span of meat?"

"Spare me. Okay, maybe they're only part meat. You know, like the weddilei. A meat head with an electron plasma[4] brain inside."

"Nope. We thought of that, since they do have meat heads, like the weddilei. But I told you, we probed them. They're meat all the way through."

"No brain?"

"Oh, there's a brain all right. It's just that the brain is *made out of meat!* That's what I've been trying to tell you."

"So . . . what does the thinking?"

"You're not understanding, are you? You're refusing to deal with what I'm telling you. The brain does the thinking. The meat."

"Thinking meat! You're asking me to believe in thinking meat!"

1. **recon** (rē′kŏn′) **vessels:** vehicles used for exploring and gathering information.
2. **sentient** (sĕn′shənt): capable of feeling sensation.
3. **orfolei:** like *weddilei* in a following sentence, an invented name for an extraterrestrial race of beings.
4. **electron plasma:** a gaslike material composed of electrons, negatively charged particles that are parts of atoms.

"Yes, thinking meat! Conscious meat! Loving meat. Dreaming meat. The meat is the whole deal! Are you beginning to get the picture, or do I have to start all over?"

"Omigod. You're serious, then. They're made out of meat."

"Thank you. Finally. Yes. They are indeed made out of meat. And they've been trying to get in touch with us for almost a hundred of their years."

"Omigod. So what does this meat have in mind?"

"First it wants to talk to us. Then I imagine it wants to explore the universe, contact other sentiences, swap ideas and information. The usual."

"We're supposed to talk to meat."

"That's the idea. That's the message they're sending out by radio. 'Hello. Anyone out there? Anybody home?' That sort of thing."

"They actually do talk, then. They use words, ideas, concepts?"

"Oh, yes. Except they do it with meat."

"I thought you just told me they used radio."

"They do, but what do you think is *on* the radio? Meat sounds. You know how when you slap or flap meat, it makes a noise? They talk by flapping their meat at each other. They can even sing by squirting air through their meat."

"Omigod. Singing meat. This is altogether too much. So what do you advise?"

"Officially or unofficially?"

"Both."

"Officially, we are required to contact, welcome, and log in any and all sentient races or multibeings in this quadrant of the universe, without prejudice, fear, or favor. Unofficially, I advise that we erase the records and forget the whole thing."

"I was hoping you would say that."

"It seems harsh, but there is a limit. Do we really want to make contact with meat?"

"I agree one hundred percent. What's there to say? 'Hello, meat. How's it going?' But will this work? How many planets are we dealing with here?"

"Just one. They can travel to other planets in special meat containers, but they can't live on them. And being meat, they can only travel through C space.[5] Which limits them to the speed of light and makes the possibility of their ever making contact pretty slim. Infinitesimal, in fact."

"So we just pretend there's no one home in the universe."

"That's it."

"Cruel. But you said it yourself, who wants to meet meat? And the ones who have been aboard our vessels, the ones you probed? You're sure they won't remember?"

"They'll be considered crackpots if they do. We went into their heads and smoothed out their meat so that we're just a dream to them."

5.   **C space:** an invented name for the space in which the visible universe exists, where—according to Einstein's special theory of relativity—no material body can travel at a speed equal to or greater than the speed of light (symbolized by the letter *c*).

"A dream to meat! How strangely appropriate, that we should be meat's dream."

"And we marked the entire sector *unoccupied.*"

"Good. Agreed, officially and unofficially. Case closed. Any others? Anyone interesting on that side of the galaxy?"

"Yes, a rather shy but sweet hydrogen core cluster intelligence in a class nine star in G445 zone. Was in contact two galactic rotations[6] ago, wants to be friendly again."

"They always come around."

"And why not? Imagine how unbearably, how unutterably cold the universe would be if one were all alone. . . ."

6.   **galactic rotations:** periods defined by the time it takes our galaxy, the Milky Way, to complete a full rotation about its center (about 225 million years).

C. REFLECTING AND RETHINKING

Review the responses you wrote as you read the story. Then, choose **one** of the options below, and answer the question at the bottom of the page.

Option One   Write your responses to the following questions.

1. What can you gather about who the two characters are, and what they are refusing to do and why?

_____

_____

_____

2. What is your reaction to the last line of the story?

_____

_____

Option Two   With a partner, assume the roles of the two characters, and read the last page of the story aloud. Then, in the boxes below, sketch the images you have in your mind of the characters and the "meat" they are talking about. Then label the attitude the characters have toward the meat.

Characters	Meat

Attitude

Additional Comments Is there anything else you'd like to say or ask about this story? Write it here.

_____

_____

D. SHARING WITH OTHERS

With a small group of classmates, share your responses from the previous activity. To make sure that everyone in the group has a chance to speak, each person should take a turn to respond while everyone else listens. Then as a group, discuss the following questions.

1. Think about the attitudes expressed by the characters in this story of first contact. What group of people from Unit One or from your own experience do these characters remind you of? Record your own and other group members' answers in the chart below.

Whom Do the Characters Resemble?	In What Ways?

2. How do you think the author wanted this story to affect readers? Write your own answer below, then share it with your group.

_____

_____

_____

_____

E. RESPONDING IN WRITING

Choose **one** of the following writing prompts and write your response on the paper given to you by your teacher.

Writing Prompt Option One   Think of an instance when you went someplace for the first time—perhaps arriving in a foreign country, a new community, or a new school. What struck you as surprising or unusual? Write an eyewitness report recounting your experience.

> In your eyewitness report, make sure you
>
> - focus on an event that has personal or historical significance
> - answer the five *W's: who, what, when, where,* and *why*
> - create a sense of immediacy using precise language and sensory images
> - present events in a clear, logical order
> - capture the mood of the event

Writing Prompt Option Two   Think of your own "first encounter" with someone, perhaps a classmate or a neighbor, who was very different from you. Perhaps he or she was of a different heritage or had beliefs different from your own. In a reflective essay, describe this encounter and discuss its significance in your life. Consider, in particular, how your views of the encounter have changed over time.

> In your reflective essay, make sure you
>
> - write in the first person
> - use figurative language, dialogue, sensory details, or other techniques to re-create the experience for the reader
> - explain the significance of the event
> - make an observation about life based on the experience
> - encourage readers to think about the significance of the experience in light of their own lives

If you have finished your writing before the allotted time is up, go back over your work for errors in grammar, punctuation, spelling, and capitalization. Mistakes in these areas can affect your score if they make your writing hard to understand. Use proofreading marks to indicate any changes that you wish to make.

Unit Two: Integrated Assessment

Reading, Writing, Speaking and Listening

INSTRUCTIONS

You'll be spending about 90 minutes reading and responding to the poem "Suzie Wong Doesn't Live Here." At different times, you will be working alone and with a small group of classmates.

This booklet is the place for you to write down all your thoughts about the selection—your first impressions as well as other ideas you have as you continue to think about and discuss the selection. In evaluating this booklet, your teacher will look at all of your writing, so please respond as completely and as honestly as you can.

In evaluating your reading, your teacher will look at how well you

- connect ideas in the selection to your own experience
- understand the tone and theme of the selection

In evaluating your writing, your teacher will look at how well you

- state your main ideas
- give details and examples to support your ideas
- organize your thoughts

In evaluating your speaking and listening, your teacher will look at how well you

- contribute to group discussion
- listen to other group members
- stay on task during the group activity
- cooperate with other group members

A. BEFORE YOU READ

Think about ways in which a particular group you belong to is stereotyped, or perceived according to a fixed notion. For example, certain stereotypes are associated with teenagers, cheerleaders, New Yorkers, or computer hackers. In the space below, draw a cartoon to represent the stereotype of your group, with labels describing characteristics linked to the stereotype, such as "bad acne" or "no social skills."

B. READING AND RESPONDING

Read the peom "Suzie Wong Doesn't Live Here." As you read, write down your thoughts and reactions in the box below. To help you with responses, use the active reading strategies: **question, connect, predict, clarify,** and **evaluate.**

If you'd prefer to divide the poem into sections, follow these guidelines:

• Read the poem through line 11, then stop and write your responses to what you have read so far.

• Continue reading through line 25. Stop again and write your responses.

• Continue to the end of the poem. Then write your responses.

It's best to read the complete poem at least three times.

NOTES

Suzie Wong Doesn't Live Here

Diane Mei Lin Mark

NOTES

Suzie Wong
doesn't live here anymore
yeah, and
Madame Butterfly
5   and the geisha ladies have all
gone
to
lunch (hey, they might
   be gone a very
10   long
   time)

no one here
but
ourselves

15   stepping on,
without downcast eyes,
without calculating dragon power,
without tight red cheongsams[1]
   embroidered with peonies
20   without the
silence
that you've come to
know so well
and we,
25   to feel so alien with

seeing each other at last
so little needs to be explained

there is this strength

1.   **cheongsams** (chĕ-ong'sam'): high-necked, close-fitting dresses with a side-slit skirt, traditionally worn by women in China and Hong Kong.

born female in Asian America,
30 our dreams stored years
in the backrooms
of our minds

now happening—
like sounds of flowers
35 bathed in noontime light
reaching righteously skyward!

C. REFLECTING AND RETHINKING

Review the responses you wrote as you read the poem. Then choose **one** of the options below to help you build your understanding.

Option One Write your response to the following questions.

1. Whom do you think the speaker is addressing as "you," and whom do "they," "we," and "ourselves" refer to?

_____

_____

_____

2. How do the women described at the beginning of the poem compare to the women described at the end?

_____

_____

_____

Option Two In the boxes, draw pictures of who "doesn't live here" and who does. Then on the lines, write captions to explain your pictures.

Who Doesn't Live Here:	Who Does:

_____   _____

_____   _____

D. SHARING WITH OTHERS

With a small group of classmates, share your responses from the previous activity. Make sure that everyone in the group has a chance to speak. Then discuss the following questions in your group, recording your own and others' answers in the chart below.

1. How would you describe the tone, or writer's attitude, in this poem?

2. How would you summarize the theme?

3. How similar to the speaker's reaction are your own reactions to being stereotyped? Explain.

E. RESPONDING IN WRITING

Choose **one** of the following writing prompts and write your response on the paper given to you by your teacher.

Writing Prompt Option One   Write a persuasive essay condemning the stereotyping of a group you belong to, as Diane Mei Lin Mark condemns the stereotyping of Asian-American women. You might use the cartoon you drew in section A as a starting point for your paper.

In your persuasive essay, make sure to

- state the issue and your position on it clearly in the introduction
- appeal to the audience you're trying to convince
- support your position with evidence, such as facts and examples
- answer possible objections to your position
- show clear reasoning
- conclude with a summary of your position or a call to action

Writing Prompt Option Two   Think of a film or television show you have seen in which a character who is at first perceived as "different" eventually is accepted by the other characters he or she encounters. Write a critical review of the film or show using the guidelines below.

In your critical review, make sure to

- identify and give a brief summary of the work
- state your opinion of the work and make clear the criteria you used to judge it
- support your opinion with well-chosen details and examples from the text
- organize arguments and supporting details in a way that is easy to follow
- conclude with a recommendation to the reader regarding the work

If you have finished your writing before the allotted time is up, go back over your work for errors in grammar, punctuation, spelling, and capitalization. Mistakes in these areas can affect your score if they make your writing hard to understand. Use proofreading marks to indicate any changes that you wish to make.

Unit Three: Integrated Assessment

Reading, Writing, Speaking and Listening

INSTRUCTIONS

You'll be spending about 90 minutes reading and responding to the selection "A Blizzard Under Blue Sky." At different times, you will be working alone, with a partner, and with a small group of classmates.

This booklet is the place for you to write down all your thoughts about the selection—your first impressions as well as other ideas you have as you continue to think about and discuss the selection. In evaluating this booklet, your teacher will look at all of your writing, so please respond as completely and as honestly as you can.

In evaluating your reading, your teacher will look at how well you

- connect ideas in the selection to your own experience
- analyze setting and character in the selection
- understand the theme of the selection

In evaluating your writing, your teacher will look at how well you

- state your main ideas
- give details and examples to support your ideas
- organize your thoughts

In evaluating your speaking and listening, your teacher will look at how well you

- contribute to group discussion
- listen to other group members
- stay on task during the group activity
- cooperate with other group members

A. BEFORE YOU READ

If you had a friend who was sad or depressed, what would you advise him or her to do? Write down your ideas for a cure in the box below.

Cure for sadness or depression:

B. READING AND RESPONDING

Read the story "A Blizzard Under Blue Sky." As you read, write down your thoughts and reactions in the box below. To help you with these responses, use the active reading strategies: **question, connect, predict, clarify,** and **evaluate.**

If you'd prefer to divide the selection into sections, follow these guidelines:

- Read the selection until you get to the sentence on page 23, ending ". . . sharpness of the air." Stop and write your responses to what you have read so far.

- Continue reading until you finish the sentence on page 24, "Jackson started to dig first." Stop again and write your responses.

- Continue to the end of the selection. Then write your responses.

NOTES

A Blizzard Under Blue Sky

Pam Houston

NOTES

The doctor said I was clinically depressed. It was February, the month in which depression runs rampant in the inversion-cloaked Salt Lake Valley[1] and the city dwellers escape to Park City, where the snow is fresh and the sun is shining and everybody is happy, except me. In truth, my life was on the verge of more spectacular and satisfying discoveries than I had ever imagined, but of course I couldn't see that far ahead. What I saw was work that wasn't getting done, bills that weren't getting paid, and a man I'd given my heart to weekending in the desert with his ex.

The doctor said, "I can give you drugs."

I said, "No way."

She said, "The machine that drives you is broken. You need something to help you get it fixed."

I said, "Winter camping."

She said, "Whatever floats your boat."

One of the things I love the most about the natural world is the way it gives you what's good for you even if you don't know it at the time. I had never been winter camping before, at least not in the high country, and the weekend I chose to try and fix my machine was the same weekend the air mass they called the Alaska Clipper showed up. It was thirty-two degrees below zero in town on the night I spent in my snow cave. I don't know how cold it was out on Beaver Creek. I had listened to the weather forecast, and to the advice of my housemate, Alex, who was an experienced winter camper.

"I don't know what you think you're going to prove by freezing to death," Alex said, "but if you've got to go, take my bivvy sack[2]; it's warmer than anything you have."

"Thanks," I said.

"If you mix Kool-Aid with your water it won't freeze up," he said, "and don't forget lighting paste for your stove."

"Okay," I said.

"I hope it turns out to be worth it," he said, "because you are going to freeze your butt."

When everything in your life is uncertain, there's nothing quite like the clarity and precision of fresh snow and blue sky. That was the first thought I had on Saturday morning as I stepped away from the warmth of my truck and

1. **inversion-cloaked . . . Valley:** The valley is frequently filled with haze and pollution because of an unfortunate mix of atmospheric conditions and landforms. In a temperature inversion, a layer of warm air traps cooler air—and pollution—near the surface of the earth, preventing the normal circulation of air.
2. **bivvy sack:** loose, watertight bag used in addition to a sleeping bag for extra protection from the cold and wet. *Bivvy* is short for *bivouac,* a temporary camp.

let my skis slap the snow in front of me. There was no wind and no clouds that morning, just still air and cold sunshine. The hair in my nostrils froze almost immediately. When I took a deep breath, my lungs only filled up halfway.

I opened the tailgate to excited whines and whimpers. I never go skiing without Jackson and Hailey: my two best friends, my yin and yang[3] of dogs. Some of you might know Jackson. He's the oversized sheepdog-and-something-else with the great big nose and the bark that will shatter glass. He gets out and about more than I do. People I've never seen before come by my house daily and call him by name. He's all grace, and he's tireless; he won't go skiing with me unless I let him lead. Hailey is not so graceful, and her body seems in constant indecision when she runs. When we ski she stays behind me, and on the downhills she tries to sneak rides on my skis.

The dogs ran circles in the chest-high snow while I inventoried my backpack one more time to make sure I had everything I needed. My sleeping bag, my Thermarest, my stove, Alex's bivvy sack, matches, lighting paste, flashlight, knife. I brought three pairs of long underwear—tops and bottoms—so I could change once before I went to bed, and once again in the morning, so I wouldn't get chilled by my own sweat. I brought paper and pen, and Kool-Aid to mix with my water. I brought Mountain House chicken stew and some freeze-dried green peas, some peanut butter and honey, lots of dried apricots, coffee and Carnation instant breakfast for morning.

Jackson stood very still while I adjusted his backpack. He carries the dog food and enough water for all of us. He takes himself very seriously when he's got his pack on. He won't step off the trail for any reason, not even to chase rabbits, and he gets nervous and angry if I do. That morning he was impatient with me. "Miles to go, Mom," he said over his shoulder. I snapped my boots into my skis and we were off.

There are not too many good things you can say about temperatures that dip past twenty below zero, except this: They turn the landscape into a crystal palace and they turn your vision into Superman's. In the cold thin morning air the trees and mountains, even the twigs and shadows, seemed to leap out of the background like a 3-D movie, only it was better than 3-D because I could feel the sharpness of the air.

I have a friend in Moab who swears that Utah is the center of the fourth dimension,[4] and although I know he has in mind something much different and more complicated than subzero weather, it was there, on that ice-edged morning, that I felt on the verge of seeing something more than depth perception in the brutal clarity of the morning sun.

As I kicked along the first couple of miles, I noticed the sun crawling higher in the sky and yet the day wasn't really warming, and I wondered if I should have brought another vest, another layer to put between me and the cold night ahead.

3. **yin and yang:** In the Chinese philosophy Taoism, *yin* is the positive, passive, female force in the universe; *yang* is the negative, active, male force.
4. **fourth dimension:** time; the first three dimensions are length, width, and depth (or height).

It was utterly quiet out there, and what minimal noise we made intruded on the morning like a brass band: the squeaking of my bindings, the slosh of the water in Jackson's pack, the whoosh of nylon, the jangle of dog tags. It was the bass line and percussion to some primal song, and I kept wanting to sing to it, but I didn't know the words.

Jackson and I crested the top of a hill and stopped to wait for Hailey. The trail stretched out as far as we could see into the meadow below us and beyond, a double track and pole plants carving through softer trails of rabbit and deer.

"Nice place," I said to Jackson, and his tail thumped the snow underneath him without sound.

We stopped for lunch near something that looked like it could be a lake in its other life, or maybe just a womb-shaped meadow. I made peanut butter and honey sandwiches for all of us, and we opened the apricots.

"It's fabulous here," I told the dogs. "But so far it's not working."

There had never been anything wrong with my life that a few good days in the wilderness wouldn't cure, but there I sat in the middle of all those crystal-coated trees, all that diamond-studded sunshine, and I didn't feel any better. Apparently clinical depression was not like having a bad day, it wasn't even like having a lot of bad days, it was more like a house of mirrors, it was like being in a room full of one-way glass.

"Come on, Mom," Jackson said. "Ski harder, go faster, climb higher."

Hailey turned her belly to the sun and groaned.

"He's right," I told her. "It's all we can do."

After lunch the sun had moved behind our backs, throwing a whole different light on the path ahead of us. The snow we moved through stopped being simply white and became translucent, hinting at other colors, reflections of blues and purples and grays. I thought of Moby Dick, you know, the whiteness of the whale, where white is really the absence of all color, and whiteness equals truth, and Ahab's[5] search is finally futile, as he finds nothing but his own reflection.

"Put your mind where your skis are," Jackson said, and we made considerably better time after that.

The sun was getting quite low in the sky when I asked Jackson if he thought we should stop to build the snow cave, and he said he'd look for the next good bank. About one hundred yards down the trail we found it, a gentle slope with eastern exposure that didn't look like it would cave in under any circumstances. Jackson started to dig first.

Let me make one thing clear. I knew only slightly more about building snow caves than Jackson, having never built one, and all my knowledge coming from disaster tales of winter camping fatalities. I knew several things *not* to do when building a snow cave, but I was having a hard time knowing what exactly to do. But Jackson helped, and Hailey supervised, and before too long we had a little

5. **Moby Dick . . . Ahab's:** In Herman Melville's novel *Moby Dick,* the title character is an extraordinary white whale of legendary cunning, and Ahab is the whaling-ship captain who pursues the whale at the cost of his own life.

cave built, just big enough for three. We ate dinner quite pleased with our accomplishments and set the bivvy sack up inside the cave just as the sun slipped away and dusk came over Beaver Creek.

The temperature, which hadn't exactly soared during the day, dropped twenty degrees in as many minutes, and suddenly it didn't seem like such a great idea to change my long underwear. The original plan was to sleep with the dogs inside the bivvy sack but outside the sleeping bag, which was okay with Jackson the super-metabolizer,[6] but not so with Hailey, the couch potato. She whined and wriggled and managed to stuff her entire fat body down inside my mummy bag, and Jackson stretched out full-length on top.

One of the unfortunate things about winter camping is that it has to happen when the days are so short. Fourteen hours is a long time to lie in a snow cave under the most perfect of circumstances. And when it's thirty-two below, or forty, fourteen hours seems like weeks.

I wish I could tell you I dropped right off to sleep. In truth, fear crept into my spine with the cold and I never closed my eyes. Cuddled there, amid my dogs and water bottles, I spent half of the night chastising myself for thinking I was Wonder Woman, not only risking my own life but the lives of my dogs, and the other half trying to keep the numbness in my feet from crawling up to my knees. When I did doze off, which was actually more like blacking out than dozing off, I'd come back to my senses wondering if I had frozen to death, but the alternating pain and numbness that started in my extremities and worked its way into my bones convinced me I must still be alive.

It was a clear night, and every now and again I would poke my head out of its nest of down and nylon to watch the progress of the moon across the sky. There is no doubt that it was the longest and most uncomfortable night of my life.

But then the sky began to get gray, and then it began to get pink, and before too long the sun was on my bivvy sack, not warm, exactly, but holding the promise of warmth later in the day. And I ate apricots and drank Kool-Aid-flavored coffee and celebrated the rebirth of my fingers and toes, and the survival of many more important parts of my body. I sang "Rocky Mountain High" and "If I Had a Hammer," and yodeled and whistled, and even danced the two-step with Jackson and let him lick my face. And when Hailey finally emerged from the sleeping bag a full hour after I did, we shared a peanut butter and honey sandwich and she said nothing ever tasted so good.

We broke camp and packed up and kicked in the snow cave with something resembling glee.

I was five miles down the trail before I realized what had happened. Not once in that fourteen-hour night did I think about deadlines, or bills, or the man in the desert. For the first time in many months I was happy to see a day beginning. The morning sunshine was like a present from the gods. What really happened, of course, is that I remembered about joy.

6. **super-metabolizer:** Metabolism is the process by which the body changes food into energy. The narrator is saying that Jackson's metabolism is so efficient that he has a great deal of energy.

I know that one night out at thirty-two below doesn't sound like much to those of you who have climbed Everest or run the Iditarod[7] or kayaked to Antarctica, and I won't try to convince you that my life was like the movies where depression goes away in one weekend, and all of life's problems vanish with a moment's clear sight. The simple truth of the matter is this: On Sunday I had a glimpse outside of the house of mirrors, on Saturday I couldn't have seen my way out of a paper bag. And while I was skiing back toward the truck that morning, a wind came up behind us and swirled the snow around our bodies like a blizzard under blue sky. And I was struck by the simple perfection of the snowflakes, and startled by the hopefulness of sun on frozen trees.

7. **Iditarod:** a very strenuous dogsled race run each year in Alaska.

C. REFLECTING AND RETHINKING
Choose **one** of the options below to help you build your understanding of the selection.

Option One   Write your responses to the following questions.

1. What is your opinion of the narrator's cure for depression? Do you feel that she was right to seek a cure in nature on her own, rather than by taking medication? Why or why not?

_____

_____

_____

2. Why do you think the narrator feels better at the end of the story?

_____

_____

_____

Option Two   Think about the emotions and sensations the narrator has at various points in the story: at the beginning before she goes camping; when she is skiing with her dogs during the day; when she is in the snow cave at night; and at the end when she wakes up in the morning. Then get together with a partner. Using only facial expressions and gestures, take turns acting out the narrator's feelings at one of these points in the story, and see if your partner can guess which point it is. Finally, on the lines below, summarize the feelings the narrator has over the course of the story.

1. Beginning

_____

_____

2. Day

_____

_____

3. Night

_____

_____

4. Morning

_____

_____

D. SHARING WITH OTHERS

Complete **both** parts of this section.

Part One Pam Houston's use of description is particularly effective in this story, re-creating both the narrator's physical experience in the natural setting and her emotional experience. Get together with a small group of classmates and look back through the story for **two** passages that you think describe the setting exceptionally well. Then talk about what the passages reveal about the narrator's inner feeling or state of mind. Complete the chart below with your group's findings. You don't have to write down the whole passage; just the beginning and end phrases separated by ellipsis points and followed by the page number (For example: "The doctor said I was . . . desert with his ex." p. 22).

Passage	Shows What Inner State?
1.	
2.	

Part Two The narrator says, near the beginning of the story, "One of the things I love most about the natural world is the way it gives you what's good for you even if you don't know it at the time." What does the natural world give to the narrator? Discuss this question in your group, then write your answer on the lines below.

_____

_____

_____

E. RESPONDING IN WRITING

Choose **one** of the following writing prompts and write your response on the paper given to you by your teacher.

Writing Prompt Option One   In the course of this story, the author learned an important lesson about herself and her life. Think about an experience you have had, or someone you admire has had, that taught an important lesson about life. Then in a reflective essay, describe this experience and explain its significance.

In your reflective essay, make sure to
- write it in the first person
- describe an important experience in your life or in the life of someone you admire
- use figurative language, dialogue, sensory details, or other techniques to re-create the experience for the reader
- explain the significance of the event
- make an observation about life based on the experience
- encourage readers to think about the significance of the experience in light of their own lives

Writing Prompt Option Two   What was your overall opinion of "A Blizzard Under Blue Sky"? Which elements of the story made you respond in that way? Write a critical review of the story in which you explain your opinion and tell to whom (if anyone) you would recommend it.

In your critical review, make sure to
- identify and give a brief summary of the work
- state your opinion of the work and make clear the criteria you used to judge it
- support your opinion with well-chosen details and examples from the text
- organize arguments and supporting details in a way that is easy to follow
- conclude with a recommendation to the reader regarding the work

If you have finished your writing before the allotted time is up, go back over your work for errors in grammar, punctuation, spelling, and capitalization. Mistakes in these areas can affect your score if they make your writing hard to understand. Use proofreading marks to indicate any changes that you wish to make.

Unit Four: Integrated Assessment

Reading, Writing, Speaking and Listening

INSTRUCTIONS

You'll be spending about 90 minutes reading and responding to the selection "Foreign Critics." At different times, you will be working alone, with a partner, and with a small group of classmates.

This booklet is the place for you to write down all your thoughts about the selection—your first impressions as well as other ideas you have as you continue to think about and discuss the selection. In evaluating this booklet, your teacher will look at all of your writing, so please respond as completely and as honestly as you can.

In evaluating your reading, your teacher will look at how well you

- connect ideas in the selection to your own experience
- understand the main idea of the selection
- analyze the author's thoughts, feelings, and ideas

In evaluating your writing, your teacher will look at how well you

- state your main ideas
- give details and examples to support your ideas
- organize your thoughts

In evaluating your speaking and listening, your teacher will look at how well you

- contribute to group discussion
- listen to other group members
- stay on task during the group activity
- cooperate with other group members

A. BEFORE YOU READ

In this selection, Mark Twain expresses the sentiment that America has been unfairly criticized by a foreign critic who thinks that the United States does not have a "real" civilization. How do you think you would respond to the critic's statement? Take a few minutes to express your personal reaction to the critic's statement and explain whether you think it was fair or unfair.

How I would respond to the foreign critic:

B. READING AND RESPONDING

Read the selection "Foreign Critics." As you read, write down your thoughts and reactions in the box below. To help you with these responses, use the active reading strategies: **question, connect, predict, clarify,** and **evaluate.**

If you'd prefer to divide the selection into sections, follow these guidelines:

- Read to the end of the second paragraph, ending with, "We made the trip and hoisted its flag when we disposed of our slavery." Stop and write your responses to what you have read so far.

- Read the rest of the selection. Then write your responses.

NOTES

Foreign Critics

Mark Twain

NOTES

If I look harried and worn, it is not from an ill conscience. It is from sitting up nights to worry about the foreign critic. He won't concede that we have a civilization—a "real" civilization. Five years ago, he said we had never contributed anything to the betterment of the world. And now comes Sir Lepel Griffin, whom I had not suspected of being in the world at all, and says, "There is no country calling itself civilized where one would not rather live than in America, except Russia." That settles it. That is, it settles it for Europe; but it doesn't make me any more comfortable than I was before.

What is "real" civilization? Nobody can answer that conundrum. They have all tried. Then suppose we try to get at what it is not, and then subtract the what it is not from the general sum, and call the remainder "real" civilization—so as to have a place to stand on while we throw bricks at these people. Let us say, then, in broad terms, that any system which has in it any one of these things—to wit, human slavery, despotic government, inequality, numerous and brutal punishments for crime, superstition almost universal, ignorance almost universal, and dirt and poverty almost universal—is not a real civilization, and any system which has none of them is. If you grant these terms, one may then consider this conundrum: How old is real civilization? The answer is easy and unassailable. A century ago it had not appeared anywhere in the world during a single instant since the world was made. If you grant these terms—and I don't see why it shouldn't be fair, since civilization must surely be fair, since civilization must surely mean the humanizing of a people, not a class—there is to-day but one real civilization in the world, and it is not yet thirty years old. We made the trip and hoisted its flag when we disposed of our slavery.

However, there are some partial civilizations scattered around over Europe—pretty lofty civilizations they are, too—but who begot them? What is the seed from which they sprang? Liberty and intelligence. What planted that seed? There are dates and statistics which suggest that it was the American Revolution that planted it. When that revolution began, monarchy had been on trial some thousands of years, over there, and was a distinct and convicted failure, every time. It had never produced anything but a vast, a nearly universal savagery, with a thin skim of civilization on top, and the main part of that was nickel plate and tinsel. The French, imbruted and impoverished by centuries of oppression and official robbery, were a starving nation clothed in rags, slaves of an aristocracy and smirking dandies clad in unearned silks and velvet. It makes one's cheek burn to read of the laws of the time and realize that they were for human beings; realize that they originated in this world and not in hell. Germany was unspeakable. In the Scotch lowlands the people lived in sties and were human swine; in the highlands drunkenness was general and it hardly smirched a young girl to have a family of her own. In England there was a sham liberty, and not much of that; crime was general; ignorance the same; poverty and misery were widespread; London fed a tenth of her population by charity; the law awarded the death penalty to almost every conceivable offense; what was called medical science by courtesy stood where it had stood for two thousand years; Tom Jones and Squire Western were gentlemen.

The printer's art had been known in Germany and France three and a quarter centuries, and in England three. In all that time there had not been a newspaper in Europe that was worthy the name. Monarchies had no use for that sort of dynamite. When we hoisted the banner of revolution and raised the first genuine shout for human liberty that had ever been heard, this was a newspaperless globe. Eight years later there were six daily journals in London to proclaim to all the nations the greatest birth this world had ever seen. Who woke that printing press out of its trance of three hundred years? Let us be permitted to consider that we did it. Who summoned the French slaves to rise and set the nation free? We did it. What resulted in England and on the Continent? Crippled liberty took up its bed and walked. From that day to this its march had not halted, and please God it never will. We are called the nation of inventors. And we are. We could still claim that title and wear its loftiest honors if we had stopped with the first thing we ever invented—which was human liberty. Out of that invention has come the Christian world's great civilization. Without it it was impossible—as the history of all the centuries has proved. Well, then, who invented civilization? Even Sir Lepel Griffin ought to be able to answer that question. It looks easy enough. *We* have contributed *nothing!* Nothing hurts me like ingratitude.

C. REFLECTING AND RETHINKING

Choose **one** of the options below to help you build your understanding of the selection.

Option One   Write your responses to the following questions.

1. Do you agree with Twain's definition of what a "real" civilization is? Do you think there are other elements that should be added to his definition? If so, what are they?

_____

_____

_____

2. Reread the last five sentences of the selection. How do you think the author feels at the end of the essay? Why does he feel this way?

_____

_____

_____

Option Two   Imagine that you are Mark Twain and you have just met Sir Lepel Griffin. What would you say to him about his opinion of America? Work with a partner and role-play this meeting. Then, on the lines below, summarize Mark Twain's feelings about Griffin's opinions of American civilization.

_____

_____

_____

_____

D. SHARING WITH OTHERS

Complete **both** parts of this section.

Part One The tone of a piece of writing is the writer's attitude toward his or her subject. With a small group of classmates, discuss the tone of this essay. Then fill in the chart below. In the first column, write two adjectives describing Twain's tone at two different points in the essay. In the second column, write one quotation from the essay that illustrates each description of the tone. In the third column, make notes giving your opinion of Twain's tone. Do you think his tone was the best way to express his feelings and ideas? Why or why not?

Description of Tone	Supporting Quotation	Opinion of Tone

Part Two Discuss the following questions in your group and record your responses below.

1. Think about Mark Twain's definition of civilization. What do you think he means when he says ". . . there is to-day but one real civilization in the world, and it is not yet thirty years old. We made the trip and hoisted its flag when we disposed of our slavery"?

2. What do you think Twain means when he says America invented "human liberty"?

E. RESPONDING IN WRITING

Choose **one** of the following writing prompts and write your response on the paper given to you by your teacher.

Writing Prompt Option One   In "Foreign Critics," Mark Twain expresses his feelings about the United States by responding to one of its critics. Think carefully about what Twain says in this essay. Then write a literary interpretation in which you explain the meaning of this selection.

> In your literary interpretation, make sure to
>
> - clearly identify the title and author of the literary work
> - give a clearly stated interpretation at or near the beginning of the essay
> - present evidence and quotations from the text to support the interpretation
> - take into account other interpretations and contradictory evidence

Writing Prompt Option Two   In this essay, Mark Twain expresses strong feelings about the United States. Choose an issue in your school or community that you have strong feelings about. Then write a persuasive essay that expresses your opinion of the issue. Your essay should convince others to agree with you and possibly to take some action.

> In your persuasive essay, make sure to
>
> - state the issue and your position on it clearly in the introduction
> - write for the audience you are trying to convince
> - support your position with evidence, such as facts and examples
> - answer possible objections to your position
> - show clear reasoning
> - conclude with a summary of your position or a call to action

If you have finished your writing before the allotted time is up, go back over your work for errors in grammar, punctuation, spelling, and capitalization. Mistakes in these areas can affect your score if they make your writing hard to understand. Use proofreading marks to indicate any changes that you wish to make.

Unit Five: Integrated Assessment
....
Reading, Writing, Speaking and Listening

INSTRUCTIONS

You'll be spending about 90 minutes reading and responding to the selections "Working Girls" and "What Work Is." At different times, you will be working alone, with a partner, and with a small group of classmates.

   This booklet is the place for you to write down all your thoughts about the poems—your first impressions as well as other ideas you have as you continue to think about and discuss the selections. In evaluating this booklet, your teacher will look at all of your writing, so please respond as completely and as honestly as you can.

   In evaluating your reading, your teacher will look at how well you

   • connect ideas in the selections to your own experience

   • analyze the thoughts and feelings of the speaker of each poem

   • understand the themes of the poems

   In evaluating your writing, your teacher will look at how well you

   • state your main idea

   • give details and examples to support your ideas

   • organize your thoughts

   In evaluating your speaking and listening, your teacher will look at how well you

   • contribute to group discussion

   • listen to other group members

   • stay on task during the group activity

   • cooperate with other group members

A. BEFORE YOU READ

The idea of working hard to achieve something has always been an important part of the American dream. However, people have different attitudes toward work. Think about your experience with the world of work—looking for a job, working at a particular job, or perhaps watching other people who go to work every day. How did you feel about your experience with work? Fill in the chart below. In the first column, briefly describe your experience. In the second column, write some words or phrases that describe your feelings about this experience.

My Experience with Work	My Feelings About This Experience

B. READING AND RESPONDING

Read the poems "Working Girls" and "What Work Is." As you read each poem, write down your thoughts and reactions in the boxes below. To help you with these responses, use the active reading strategies: **question, connect, predict, clarify,** and **evaluate.** Read each poem three times.

"Working Girls"	"What Work Is"

Working Girls

Carl Sandburg

The working girls in the morning are going to work—long lines of them afoot amid the downtown stores and factories, thousands with little brick-shaped lunches wrapped in newspapers under their arms.

Each morning as I move through this river of young-woman life I feel a wonder about where it is all going, so many with a peach bloom of young years on them and laughter of red lips and memories in their eyes of dances the night before and plays and walks.

Green and gray streams run side by side in a river and so here are always the others, those who have been over the way, the women who know each one the end of life's gamble for her, the meaning and the clue, the how and the why of the dances and the arms that passed around their waists and the fingers that played in their hair.

Faces go by written over: "I know it all, I know where the bloom and the laughter go and I have memories," and the feet of these move slower and they have wisdom where the others have beauty.

So the green and the gray move in the early morning on the downtown streets.

What Work Is

Philip Levine

We stand in the rain in a long line
waiting at Ford Highland Park. For work.
You know what work is—if you're
old enough to read this you know what
work is, although you may not do it.
Forget you. This is about waiting,
shifting from one foot to another.
Feeling the light rain falling like mist
into your hair, blurring your vision
until you think you see your own brother
ahead of you, maybe ten places.
You rub your glasses with your fingers,
and of course it's someone else's brother,
narrower across the shoulders than
yours but with the same sad slouch, the grin
that does not hide the stubbornness,
the sad refusal to give in to
rain, to the hours wasted waiting,
to the knowledge that somewhere ahead
a man is waiting who will say, "No,
we're not hiring today," for any
reason he wants. You love your brother,
now suddenly you can hardly stand
the love flooding you for your brother,
who's not beside you or behind or
ahead because he's home trying to
sleep off a miserable night shift
at Cadillac so he can get up
before noon to study his German.
Works eight hours a night so he can sing
Wagner, the opera you hate most,
the worst music ever invented.
How long has it been since you told him
you loved him, held his wide shoulders,
opened your eyes wide and said those words,
and maybe kissed his cheek? You've never
done something so simple, so obvious,
not because you're too young or too dumb,
not because you're jealous or even mean
or incapable of crying in
the presence of another man, no,
just because you don't know what work is.

NOTES

C. REFLECTING AND RETHINKING

Choose **one** of the options below to help you build your understanding of the poems.

Option One   Write your responses to the following questions.

1. According to the speaker in "Working Girls," how are the young working girls and the older working women different?

_____

_____

_____

2. What feelings does the speaker of "What Work Is" express about his brother?

_____

_____

_____

Option Two   Think about the picture or image you see in your mind as you read each of these poems. In the first box, draw a picture of what you see when you read "Working Girls." In the second box, draw a picture of what you see as you read "What Work Is." (If you can't capture what you see by drawing, then make a rough sketch and write notes describing what each picture would look like.) Then, on the lines, write captions to explain your pictures.

"Working Girls"	**"What Work Is"**

Caption: _____   **Caption:** _____

D. SHARING WITH OTHERS

Complete **both** parts of this section.

Part One With a small group of classmates, discuss the meaning of the quotation from each poem in the chart below. Fill in the chart with the interpretation that you think is the best.

Quotation	What It Means
from "Working Girls": "Green and gray streams run side by side in a river and so here are always the others, those who have been over the way, the women who know each one the end of life's gamble for her. . . ."	
from "What Work Is": "How long has it been since you told him / you loved him, held his wide shoulders, / opened your eyes wide and said those words, / and maybe kissed his cheek? You've never / done something so simple, so obvious, / . . . just because you don't know what work is."	

Part Two The speakers of these two poems express their feelings about working and about life in general in very different ways. With your group, compare the thoughts and feelings the speaker expresses in each poem and how he expresses them. Then discuss what you think the theme or main idea about life is in each poem. In your discussion, consider the main themes of the unit, "Women's Voices, Women's Lives" and "The American Dream." Then write your answer on the lines below.

_____

_____

_____

_____

_____

_____

E. RESPONDING IN WRITING

Choose **one** of the following writing prompts and write your response on the paper given to you by your teacher.

Writing Prompt Option One   Write a comparison-and-contrast essay in which you explore how "Working Girls" and "What Work Is" are similar and how they are different. In your essay, you might choose to compare and contrast the use of imagery or the mood in each poem; the themes or main ideas; or how the speakers feel about what they describe.

> In your comparison-and-contrast essay, make sure to
>
> - identify the subjects being compared
>
> - establish a clear reason for the comparison
>
> - include both similarities and differences and support them with specific examples and details
>
> - follow a clear organizational pattern
>
> - use transitional words and phrases to make the relationships among ideas clear
>
> - summarize the comparison in the conclusion

Writing Prompt Option Two   In each of these poems, the speaker describes a situation in which he is part of a crowd. One is surrounded by people hurrying to work, the other is in a long line of people seeking jobs. Think about a time when you were in a crowd and write an eyewitness report describing your experience.

> In your eyewitness report, make sure to
>
> - focus on the event described in one of the poems
>
> - answer the five *W*'s: *who, what, when, where,* and *why*
>
> - create a sense of immediacy using precise language and sensory images
>
> - present events in a clear, logical order
>
> - capture the mood of the event

If you have finished your writing before the allotted time is up, go back over your work for errors in grammar, punctuation, spelling, and capitalization. Mistakes in these areas can affect your score if they make your writing hard to understand. Use proofreading marks to indicate any changes that you wish to make.

Unit Six: Integrated Assessment

Reading, Writing, Speaking and Listening

INSTRUCTIONS

You'll be spending about 90 minutes reading and responding to the selection "Whatever Happened to Spare Time?" At different times, you will be working alone, with a partner, and with a small group of classmates.

This booklet is the place for you to write down all your thoughts about the selection—your first impressions as well as other ideas you have as you continue to think about and discuss the selection. In evaluating this booklet, your teacher will look at all of your writing, so please respond as completely and as honestly as you can.

In evaluating your reading, your teacher will look at how well you

- connect ideas in the selection to your own experience
- understand the theme or main idea of the selection
- recognize how the author develops the theme

In evaluating your writing, your teacher will look at how well you

- state your main ideas
- give details and examples to support your ideas
- organize your thoughts

In evaluating your speaking and listening, your teacher will look at how well you

- contribute to group discussion
- listen to other group members
- stay on task during the group activity
- cooperate with other group members

A. BEFORE YOU READ

How do we use our leisure time in today's increasingly busy society? Think about what your free time means to you and how you use it. In your free time, do you participate in activities with friends, or do you enjoy being alone? Or are you so worried about using your time productively that having free time isn't really much fun at all? Take a few minutes to freewrite about the free time in your life. In your description, briefly describe how you use your free time. Then, jot down a few words or expressions that explain how you feel about it.

What I do in my free time:

My feelings about my free time:

B. READING AND RESPONDING

Read the essay "Whatever Happened To Spare Time?" As you read, write down your thoughts and reactions in the box below. To help you with these responses, use the active reading strategies: **question, connect, predict, clarify,** and **evaluate.**

If you'd prefer to divide the selection into sections, follow these guidelines and write your responses after you read each section:

- Read the first five paragraphs, ending with, ". . . or stroll like zombies through shopping malls?"

- Read the next four paragraphs, ending with, "Phone home."

- Read the remainder of the selection.

NOTES

Whatever Happened to Spare Time?

Michael Posner

A friend of mine, a sales executive named Daniel, was complaining the other day about work. The burden of his complaint was that, except for sleep, he seemed to be working constantly. His alarm woke him daily at 6 a.m.; an hour later he was showered, shaved, suited up, and fed, armed not only with an obligatory coffee and danish but also with essential information: the morning television news, reminder memos on his electronic pocket diary, overnight faxes from distant envoys. He was at his desk by 7:20. Typically, he worked through lunch, stayed late, and filled his briefcase with files and required reading for the evenings. By the end of most weeks, he had spent about 55 hours in the office, another 15 hours working at home, and roughly the same number in social activities—dinners, receptions, rounds of golf—that really constituted work by another name. It was, he concluded, slavery.

At first glance, the proposition that late-20th-century North Americans might enjoy less leisure than earlier generations seems preposterous. Arithmetically, in fact, it is preposterous: In 1910, the official work week was 50 hours; today it is 38. As recently as 1950, most households did not have washing machines, dishwashers, electric lawnmowers, microwave ovens, or other labor-saving devices. Today, we live longer, take extended holidays, retire earlier. To fill the extra time, leisure and recreation industries have expanded exponentially. We have more free time, and more choice of how to fill that time, than any civilization in history. As U.S. communications theorist Neil Postman has observed, ours is a civilization in danger of amusing itself to death.

Yet Daniel is hardly an aberration. When he looks around, most of his peers, his bosses, and his subordinates are working just as hard. Indeed, there is growing evidence, both quantitative and anecdotal, that at least among the professional executive classes—the management elite—a contrary phenomenon is simultaneously under way: Leisure is in retreat. For some, the amount of free time is actually declining. For others, the narcotic of work has seriously impaired the ability to enjoy leisure. And for still others, as the economist Ralph Glaser predicted, "the problem is not so much to get leisure; it is to know what to fill it with."

This is not, of course, strictly a North American phenomenon. An estimated 10,000 Japanese a year die of overwork—roughly the same number as die in car accidents. Nor is it exclusive to the white-collar classes. According to Statistics Canada, more than half a million Canadians engage in moonlighting. Those are the reported figures; real numbers are doubtless higher. For many, free time is just a good excuse to find another job.

The leisure problem is increasingly documented in surveys and opinion polls, but a few recent examples will suffice. In one Ontario government study of some 2,000 people, 90 percent said they did not take part in all the leisure-time activities they wanted to, chiefly because they lacked the time or the energy. Decima Research's March, 1991, *Quarterly* discloses this curious statistic: Compared with three years ago, as many people say they have less free time today as say they have more. Even when people acknowledge having more free time, a survey conducted for Hilton Hotels concluded, they report feeling that they have not used their time productively, that there is no time for fun. Almost 40 percent say they cut back on sleep to make more time. And nearly half of those polled said they would be willing to trade a day's pay for an extra day of free time. A vague unease seems to haunt our leisure. "What you're seeing," says Decima chairman Allan Gregg, "is the Protestant ethos in turmoil. People say they want more leisure, but they can't stop working. Leisure is suspect. We still think there's something bad about not working hard." Why, at the end of the century that promised the creation of the world's first leisure society, are many of us working harder than ever—or working so hard that, when we finally stop, all we seem able to do is slump in front of television sets or stroll like zombies through shopping malls?

In the age of faith, the better future was the afterlife; pain now, redemption later. The church promised salvation, and millions of otherwise miserable lives were made tolerable. After Martin Luther and printer Johann Gutenberg permitted man to talk to God directly, work was what you did to prove you were going to heaven. The harder you worked, the more valid the passport. The Industrial Revolution married capitalism to science. Industry created products; advertising made us want them; technology gave us time to use them. The era of mass leisure—and bought pleasure—had begun. Work was what you did to acquire money to buy machines that gave you time to work harder to acquire more money to buy bigger machines. Most people were too busy consuming or working to notice the irony.

The progress myth is dying. Its most glib assumption—that next year's paycheck will be fatter than this year's—is already under serious pressure. The future itself grows ever more fearsome: a minefield of toxic waste, ultraviolet radiation, nuclear menace, fetid air, bacterial water, random crime, and pandemic drugs. Even as the myth retreats, disciples of consumerism remain industrious. They continue to aspire to the bigger house, the luxury car, the time-shared villa. Voluntarily, they choose work over leisure, even when it prevents them from savoring the fruits of their labor. Among elites, certain lifestyle standards are deemed obligatory: the yacht, the winter home, the country club. Debt is the badge of membership. Consumption has become a Pavlovian reflex. Our jobs may be boring, empty, and futile, but we have been indoctrinated to believe that compact discs and Armani suits can somehow fill the void.

Corporate pressures are also exacting a toll on leisure time. Some executives will always be drawn by the cult of ambition. Our work defines us; we are what we do. And the more success we achieve, the stronger our identity. Survival strategies have forced hundreds of industries to remove whole tiers of middle and senior managers. Those who remain are working harder and longer.

Ironically, the very toys of technology that implicitly promised greater freedom—the computer, the fax machine, the cellular telephone—have bound us ever more certainly to the job. Ask any executive: The result of every new "technovation" is never less paper but more. The technology is omnipresent. A restaurant in Chicago has inaugurated a checking service for cellular telephones. Soon, maitre d's will ask patrons if they wish to be seated in phone or no-phone sections. Soon, vacationing managers will receive satellite-beamed messages on wrist phones. E.T. (executive traveler): Phone home.

The engines that drive our work habits—our materialism, ambition, and "techno-slavery"—are all pieces of a larger canvas, the empty narcissism of contemporary life. Is it merely a coincidence that the overwhelming majority of North Americans spend most of their free time watching television? The average length of any image seen on television is 3.5 seconds. The eye never rests. If the image offends, it will change or be changed by remote control. Thirty-odd channels are routinely available, dozens more via satellite. There are shows for every mood, meals for every appetite. Boredom is anesthetized.

In a society in which anything is instantly available, everything becomes disposable, including values. Everything must be New or Improved. But nothing is immutable, and nothing is sacred. The sacred, by definition is enduring. And if nothing endures, then the past is merely a quaint curiosity and the future largely irrelevant.

Millions of people, of course, seek leisure away from television—in bird watching and bungee jumping, golf and tennis, biking and kayaking, Club Med and Disney World. But most activities are structured and goal-directed, stripped of playfulness or genuine restfulness. People work as hard at their leisure as they do at their jobs, the paradigm being the fitness buff who rides a stationary bicycle in front of a muted TV set while reading *People* magazine and listening to music on earphones. Is this leisure?

The book of Genesis tells us that God took the seventh day off. He not only rested. He rested from all His work. He stopped creating. The distinction is important. The Ten Commandments command us to honor the Sabbath and keep it holy. To obey the injunction, we would be forced to abandon almost everything we now think of as leisure and stop creating—to think, to read, to be alone with ourselves and savor silence.

C. REFLECTING AND RETHINKING

Choose **one** of the options below to help you build your understanding of the selection.

Option One   Write your responses to the following questions.

1. The author says, "Ours is a civilization in danger of amusing itself to death." What do you think the author means by this statement?

_____

_____

_____

2. Think about the views expressed by the author of this essay and your own feelings about leisure time and the part it plays in your life. How would you compare your feelings to those of the author?

_____

_____

_____

Option Two   In this essay, the author discusses how North Americans handle job-related stress and leisure time. With a partner, role-play a conversation with someone who works at a computer company and a former co-worker who has just quit because she was overstressed. What do you think these two people would say to each other about their work and how their jobs affected their leisure time? Then, on the word web below, write down words or phrases that sum up your thoughts about leisure time in today's society.

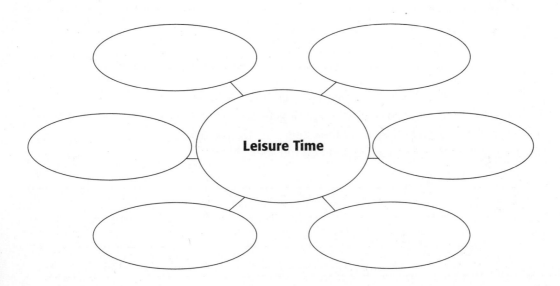

D. SHARING WITH OTHERS

Complete **both** parts of this section.

Part One Working with a small group of students, review this selection, and, in the chart below, write down three or four main ideas that answer the question posed in the title "Whatever Happened to Spare Time?" Then discuss the main ideas and find one or two details in the essay that support each idea.

Main Idea	Supporting Detail(s)

Part Two Discuss the following questions in your group and record your responses below.

1. In the first paragraph of this essay, the author describes his friend Daniel's complaints about work. Why do you think Michael Posner began his essay in this way? What effect did this paragraph have on you as you continued to read the selection?

_____

_____

_____

_____

2. In this essay, Michael Posner says about our leisure time that "most activities are structured and goal-directed, stripped of playfulness or genuine restfulness. People work as hard at their leisure as they do at their jobs . . . ." Do you agree or disagree with this statement? Explain your opinion on the lines below.

_____

_____

_____

_____

E. RESPONDING IN WRITING

Choose **one** of the following writing prompts and write your response on the paper given to you by your teacher.

Writing Prompt Option One   Think carefully about the themes of this essay and their relationship to the unit theme of the alienation of the individual. Then write a critical review of the essay in which you establish evaluation criteria and express your opinion of the selection.

In your critical review, make sure to

- identify and give a brief summary of the work

- state your opinion of the work and make clear the criteria you used to judge it

- support your opinion with well-chosen details and examples from the text

- organize arguments and supporting details in a way that is easy to follow

- conclude with a recommendation to the reader regarding the work

Writing Prompt Option Two   Think about an experience you have had in which you observed or learned something about how people view their leisure time. Write a reflective essay in which you consider this experience and share what it meant to you.

In your reflective essay, make sure to

- write in the first person

- describe an important experience in your life

- use figurative language, dialogue, sensory details, or other techniques to re-create the experience for the reader

- explain the significance of the event

- make an observation about life based on the experience

- encourage readers to think about the significance of the experience in light of their own lives

If you have finished your writing before the allotted time is up, go back over your work for errors in grammar, punctuation, spelling, and capitalization. Mistakes in these areas can affect your score if they make your writing hard to understand. Use proofreading marks to indicate any changes that you wish to make.

Unit Seven: Integrated Assessment

Reading, Writing, Speaking and Listening

INSTRUCTIONS

You'll be spending about 90 minutes reading and responding to the selection "The Lesson." At different times, you will be working alone, with a partner, and with a small group of classmates.

This booklet is the place for you to write down all your thoughts about the selection—your first impressions as well as other ideas you have as you continue to think about and discuss the selection. In evaluating this booklet, your teacher will look at all of your writing, so please respond as completely and as honestly as you can.

In evaluating your reading, your teacher will look at how well you

- connect ideas in the selection to your own experience
- understand the actions and motivations of the people in the selection and how they are presented by the writer
- analyze the theme of the selection
- understand the autobiographical elements of the selection

In evaluating your writing, your teacher will look at how well you

- state your main ideas
- give details and examples to support your ideas
- organize your thoughts

In evaluating your speaking and listening, your teacher will look at how well you

- contribute to group discussion
- listen to other group members
- stay on task during the group activity
- cooperate with other group members

A. BEFORE YOU READ

Have you ever been the outsider in a group because of the way you looked or acted? How did you feel when you were the object of ridicule from other members of the group? Did anyone step forward to help you? Take a few minutes to freewrite about such an experience, either as it happened to you or as you can imagine it happening. Or, you can draw a picture about the experience in the space below.

B. READING AND RESPONDING

Read the selection "The Lesson." As you read, write down your thoughts and reactions in the box below. To help you with these responses, use the active reading strategies: **question, connect, predict, clarify,** and **evaluate.**

If you'd prefer to divide the selection into sections, follow these guidelines:

• Read the selection until you get to the paragraph ending ". . . in recalling it now, the words hideous and ghastly come to mind."

• Read the remainder of the selection.

NOTES

The Lesson

Harry Mark Petrakis

NOTES

When I was in my green-boned youth, a little less than twelve, we lived in a neighborhood that was a village within the city. Prohibition had just been repealed, the banks had closed, and the country was in the grip of the hungry years.

Looking back from our vantage point today, everything seemed astonishingly cheap. A box of cornflakes cost eight cents, a quart of milk a dime, a dental filling a dollar. Yet inexpensive as everything might have been made little difference because money to buy anything was so scarce.

My father was a Greek Orthodox priest with his parish in a south side neighborhood. In addition to my mother, there were six children in our family, three boys and three girls. Four siblings were older than I was and a sister was younger. The four oldest worked part-time jobs and contributed to expenses. My sister and I were spared outside employment because of our ages but helped my mother in her housework and by running errands.

For a period of several years, we moved every year. I suspect those moves came because new tenants were allowed the first two months' free rent. Yet each of the apartments we occupied in the three-story buildings had the same bleak, cramped interiors, small bedrooms, like cubicles in the labyrinth of Daedalus.

The warmest and most convivial room in the apartment was always the kitchen. There my mother daily replicated the miracle of the loaves and fishes. The Greek rice dish, pilaf, was one of her staples and she prepared it several times a week in great pots. Yet with culinary cunning she dismembered one scrawny chicken into each pot of pilaf. In her wisdom she understood a morsel of poultry suggested a more wholesome meal. My sister and I, being the youngest, were often left with the less palatable parts of the fowl. But I did not know they were undesirable then and I confess those meals have left me with a propensity for the chicken's tail and neck.

The cloistered neighborhood in which we lived was populated by several ethnic and religious groups. There were Greek Orthodox and Italian Catholics, and Russian and Polish Jews. We lived and played together amicably because poverty compelled us into democracy. How could I harbor any prejudice against a Catholic or Jewish boy whose pants were ragged as mine?

Little was known of family planning then, so large families were the norm. To clothe the mob of children was an imposing challenge. The only clothing store in our neighborhood was owned by a wily shopkeeper who handled only two sizes. "A perfect fit!" or "He'll grow into it!"

In his emporium, clothing was not displayed on racks but piled in great mounds on several large tables. The piles might include a few new items but most of the clothing was used. To see a half dozen mothers foraging through piles to find garments suitable for their offspring could only be compared to an army seeking plunder.

But there was very little cash to pay for store-bought clothing whether used or new. So an energetic activity of the mothers was the ancient trade of barter.

In this exchange of clothing, my mother was a skillful contestant. She had an intuitive sense about which boys and girls in our block were outgrowing their dresses and jackets the quickest and which of these garments could be accommodated to the needs of our family.

It was true that for a good part of the year we wore as little clothing as possible. The boy's attire was a simple pair of pants, t-shirt, socks and battered sneakers. The girls wore plain dresses or shorts. However, as fall began to chill our days, we needed more durable apparel. So the first traces of colder weather compelled a frenzy of haggling. Mothers would visit one another after dinner carrying an armful of clothing. A girl's dress for a boy's shirt. A boy's blazer for a girl's jacket.

In the same way that we tended to be tolerant of one another's ethnicity and religion, we were forbearing of the shabby and mismatched clothing that graced our lithe, young bodies. Clothing was something we wore to keep us decent. From time to time some aberration drew our derision but those taunts passed quickly. That is until the appearance of the green and yellow coat.

So many years have passed since then that I wonder if I am making that coat more appalling than it really was. Lacking the vocabulary at the time to properly describe the garment, in recalling it now, the words hideous and ghastly come to mind.

The coat first appeared on a late November afternoon worn by my next-door neighbor, Seymour. He was about a year older than I was, ten pounds heavier, with a doleful demeanor. Or perhaps I remember it as doleful because the coat belonged to him.

Seymour emerged from the hallway of his building. A half dozen of us at play in the street fell silent, staring at the approaching apparition. The colors were what struck us first. A sickly green and a pallid yellow. But the colors also seemed to leak into one another so the yellow had traces of green and the green traces of yellow. In the same way, the material was indefinable, suggesting mostly a kind of frayed wool or threadbare fleece. There was also a ragged belt that Seymour wore as if it were a noose.

Seymour witnessed our collective shock and hesitated, as if pondering whether to flee back inside. By then it was too late. Our relentless taunting and mocking had begun.

All through that cold and dismal winter, Seymour wore that coat that was so ugly it offended even our primitive aesthetic senses. But since the coat was also an inanimate object, all our scorn and ridicule was hurled upon the wearer. He would have gladly thrown it away and borne the elements stoically but his parents warned him somberly that he might fall ill from exposure and die. In the end Seymour endured that winter more wretched than poor Hester Prynne in the Nathaniel Hawthorne novel we studied in school. Her letter was only scarlet while Seymour's coat was yellow and green.

Finally, the worst of winter passed. Then, on a still cold day in early March, a coatless Seymour emerged from his apartment, so buoyant and unburdened he might have been naked. Although we had some cold days later in March and in early April, Seymour never wore that coat again.

April cavorted into May and May frolicked into June. The sun grew stronger and we stripped off layers of clothing until we played, almost naked, our arms, legs and faces growing tanned from the sun.

Yet in that blustery, subzero region known as the Midwest, the sun's reign is transitory. Before we knew it, summer had passed.

As autumn arrived, we prepared for school. The mothers returned like itinerant peddlers to haggling and bartering over clothing.

On a Saturday evening my mother returned from one of the trading sessions. My sisters met her with shrieks at our front door, anxious to see the wardrobe she had assembled for them. I had not given serious attention to what clothing I needed. My mother's vigilant eye took care of that and I trusted in her judgment. That is, until I saw amidst the dresses she had brought for my sisters, the monstrous green and yellow coat she had traded to replace my own worn and outgrown coat.

I pleaded for mercy. At the same time I could not confess to her how we had all tormented poor Seymour. She was a religious lady and might have felt my inheriting the coat was evidence of divine justice. In response to my entreaties, she was sympathetic but also adamant. The coat was all I would have to wear to protect me from the implacable cold of the coming winter.

I had never faced the onslaught of any winter with greater dread than I did that year. I avoided wearing the cursed coat as long as I could. When the weather did finally turn cold I took a circuitous back-alley route to school. A half-block away I removed the coat, bunched it up, and stuffed it into a shopping bag.

In that way I managed to avoid exposure for several weeks. But on a frigid Saturday afternoon in early November my mother sent me to the grocery for eggs and bread. Despite my insistence that I'd run both ways, she made me wear the coat.

I purchased the items from the grocery, ignoring the look of pity on the grocer's face. As I emerged from the store I came face to face with a cluster of my friends about to enter the store. Seymour was with them.

I was close enough to witness the shock and disbelief on their faces. That turned quickly to sadistic glee. As their raucous taunts began, Seymour stepped forward quickly and aligned himself beside me. Staring defiantly at the jeering mob, he put his arm protectively and reassuringly around my shoulders. That gesture of defense and support from someone who had suffered our taunts through an entire winter startled the others. They could not comprehend such magnanimity of spirit and it awed and silenced them. In an awkward hush, they turned and shuffled away. And in that glowing moment, Seymour and I bonded like comrades, I understood that because of his greatness of soul, I had been spared.

Now, a lifetime later, as I recount this story, I am intemperately moved once again. What befell me then in my twelfth year of life was a lesson in tolerance and forgiveness so searing and unforgettable, it rivaled one of those Greek dramas in which my ancestors portrayed heroes and gods.

C. REFLECTING AND RETHINKING
Choose **one** of the options below to help you build your understanding of the selection.

Option One   Write your responses to the following questions.

1. What do you think of what Seymour did to help the author? Why, do you think, did Seymour act the way he did?

_____

_____

_____

_____

2. What do you think the narrator means when he writes, "We lived and played together amicably because poverty compelled us into democracy"?

_____

_____

_____

_____

Option Two   Think about how Seymour felt when the other boys, including the author, made fun of the coat he was forced to wear. Working with a partner, role-play a meeting between Seymour and one of his childhood tormentors as an adult. What do you think they might say to each other today about their childhood experiences? After your discussion, step back into your own identity as a reader and write your own analysis of why the boys in the neighborhood continued their "relentless taunting and mocking."

_____

_____

_____

_____

_____

D. SHARING WITH OTHERS
Complete **both** parts of this section.

Part One This selection is an autobiographical account of an important event from the author's childhood. Autobiographies often share certain important characteristics with fiction. For example, they often include characters, setting, plot, and a theme. This selection describes events in anecdotes, or brief stories that make a point. Working with a group of classmates, identify one anecdote from the selection. Then complete the chart below with information about the anecdote your group selected.

Event as Anecdote	Summary of Character, Setting, and Plot	Purpose of Including Anecdote

Part Two Why, do you think, did the author title this selection "The Lesson"? In your answer, explain what you think the title refers to, and identify a sentence or sentences from the selection that summarizes what the lesson is.

_____

_____

_____

_____

E. RESPONDING IN WRITING

Choose **one** of the following writing prompts and write your response on the paper given to you by your teacher.

Writing Prompt Option One   In this autobiographical selection, the author reflects on an experience that taught him an important lesson about life. Think about an experience you have had that taught you an important lesson about life. Then, in a reflective essay, describe this experience to your readers and explain its significance to you.

> In your reflective essay, make sure to
>
> - write in the first person
>
> - describe an important experience in your life
>
> - use figurative language, dialogue, sensory details, or other techniques to re-create the experience for the reader
>
> - explain the significance of the event
>
> - make an observation about life based on the experience
>
> - encourage readers to think about the significance of the experience in light of their own lives

Writing Prompt Option Two   In this selection, the author describes an event that had personal significance for him. Write your own eyewitness report of an event you saw that had personal or historical significance for you. It might be something you saw in your community or at school.

> In your eyewitness report, make sure to
>
> - focus on an event that has personal or historical significance
>
> - answer the five *W*'s: *who, what, when, where,* and *why*
>
> - create a sense of immediacy using precise language and sensory images
>
> - present events in a clear, logical order
>
> - capture the mood of the event

If you have finished your writing before the allotted time is up, go back over your work for errors in grammar, punctuation, spelling, and capitalization. Mistakes in these areas can affect your score if they make your writing hard to understand. Use proofreading marks to indicate any changes that you wish to make.

Reader

End-of-Year Integrated Assessment

Student Name _____

Date _____

If

Rudyard Kipling

NOTES

If you can keep your head when all about you
Are losing theirs and blaming it on you;
If you can trust yourself when all men doubt you,
But make allowance for their doubting too;
If you can wait and not be tired by waiting,
Or, being lied about, don't deal in lies,
Or, being hated, don't give way to hating,
And yet don't look too good, nor talk too wise;

If you can dream—and not make dreams your master;
If you can think—and not make thoughts your aim;
If you can meet with triumph and disaster
And treat those two imposters just the same;
If you can bear to hear the truth you've spoken
Twisted by knaves to make a trap for fools,
Or watch the things you gave your life to broken,
And stoop and build 'em up with wornout tools;

If you can make one heap of all your winnings
And risk it on one turn of pitch-and-toss,
And lose, and start again at your beginnings
And never breathe a word about your loss;
If you can force your heart and nerve and sinew
To serve your turn long after they are gone,
And so hold on when there is nothing in you
Except the Will which says to them: "Hold on";

If you can talk with crowds and keep your virtue,
Or walk with kings—nor lose the common touch;
If neither foes nor loving friends can hurt you;
If all men count with you, but none too much;
If you can fill the unforgiving minute
With sixty seconds' worth of distance run—
Yours is the Earth and everything that's in it,
And—which is more—you'll be a Man my son!

Polonius's Advice to Laertes *from* Hamlet

William Shakespeare

Yet here, Laertes? Aboard, aboard, for shame!
The wind sits in the shoulder of your sail,
And you are stay'd for. There—my blessing with thee!
And these few precepts in thy memory
Look thou character. Give thy thoughts no tongue,
Nor any unproportion'd thought his act.
Be thou familiar, but by no means vulgar:
Those friends thou hast, and their adoption tried,
Grapple them to thy soul with hoops of steel,
But do not dull thy palm with entertainment
Of each new-hatch'd, unfledg'd comrade. Beware
Of entrance to a quarrel, but being in,
Bear't that th' opposed may beware of thee.
Give every man thy ear, but few thy voice,
Take each man's censure, but reserve thy judgment.
Costly thy habit as thy purse can buy,
But not express'd in fancy, rich, not gaudy;
For the apparel oft proclaims the man,
And they in France of the best rank and station
Are of a most select and generous chief in that.
Neither a borrower nor a lender be;
For loan oft loses both itself and friend,
And borrowing dulleth the edge of husbandry.
This above all: to thine own self be true,
And it must follow, as the night the day,
Thou canst not then be false to any man.
Farewell, my blessing season this in thee!

NOTES

Advice to Youth

Mark Twain

NOTES

Being told I would be expected to talk here, I inquired what sort of a talk I ought to make. They said it should be something suitable to youth—something didactic, instructive, or something in the nature of good advice. Very well. I have a few things in my mind which I have often longed to say for the instruction of the young; for it is in one's tender early years that such things will best take root and be most enduring and most valuable. First, then, I will say to you, my young friends—and I say it beseechingly, urgingly—

Always obey your parents, when they are present. This is the best policy in the long run, because if you don't they will make you. Most parents think they know better than you do, and you can generally make more by humoring that superstition than you can by acting on your own better judgment.

Be respectful to your superiors, if you have any, also to strangers, and sometimes to others. If a person offend you, and you are in doubt as to whether it was intentional or not, do not resort to extreme measures; simply watch your chance and hit him with a brick. That will be sufficient. If you shall find that he had not intended any offense, come out frankly and confess yourself in the wrong when you struck him; acknowledge it like a man and say you didn't mean to. Yes, always avoid violence; in this age of charity and kindliness, the time has gone by for such things. Leave dynamite to the low and unrefined.

Go to bed early, get up early—this is wise. Some authorities say get up with the sun; some others say get up with one thing, some with another. But a lark is really the best thing to get up with. It gives you a splendid reputation with everybody to know that you get up with the lark; and if you get the right kind of a lark, and work at him right, you can easily train him to get up at half past nine, every time—it is no trick at all.

Now as to the matter of lying. You want to be very careful about lying; otherwise you are nearly sure to get caught. Once caught, you can never again be, in the eyes of the good and the pure, what you were before. Many a young person has injured himself permanently through a single clumsy and ill-finished lie, the result of carelessness born of incomplete training. Some authorities hold that the young ought not to lie at all. That, of course, is putting it rather stronger than necessary; still, while I cannot go quite so far as that, I do maintain, and I believe I am right, that the young ought to be temperate in the use of this great art until practice and experience shall give them that confidence, elegance, and precision which alone can make the accomplishment graceful and profitable. Patience, diligence, painstaking attention to detail—these are the requirements; these, in time, will make the student perfect; upon these, and upon these only, may he rely as the sure foundation for future eminence. Think what tedious years of study, thought, practice, experience, went to the equipment of that peerless old master who was able to impose upon the whole world the lofty and sounding maxim that "truth is mighty and will prevail"—the most majestic compound fracture of fact which any of woman born has yet achieved. For the history of our race, and each individual's experience, are sown thick with evidence that a truth is not hard to kill and that a lie told well is immortal. There in Boston is a monument of the man who discovered anesthesia; many people are aware, in these latter days, that that man didn't discover it at all, but stole the discovery from another man. Is this truth mighty, and will it prevail? Ah no, my hearers, the monument is made of hardy material, but the lie it tells will outlast it a million years. An awkward, feeble, leaky lie is a thing which you ought to make it your unceasing study to avoid; such a lie as that has no more real permanence than an average truth. Why, you might as well tell the truth at once and be done with it. A feeble, stupid, preposterous lie will not live two years—except it be a slander upon somebody. It is indestructible, then, of course, but that is no merit of yours. A final word: begin your practice of this gracious and beautiful art early—begin now. If I had begun earlier, I could have learned how.

Never handle firearms carelessly. The sorrow and suffering that have been caused through the innocent but heedless handling of firearms by the young! Only four days ago, right in the next farmhouse to the one where I am spending the summer, a grandmother, old and gray and sweet, one of the loveliest spirits in the land, was sitting at her work, when her young grandson crept in and got down an old, battered, rusty gun which had not been touched for many years and was supposed not to be loaded, and pointed it at her, laughing and threatening to shoot. In her fright she ran screaming and pleading toward the door on the other side of the room; but as she passed him he placed the gun almost against her very breast and pulled the trigger! He had supposed it was not loaded. And he was right—it wasn't. So there wasn't any harm done. It is the only case of that kind I ever heard of. Therefore, just the same, don't you meddle with old unloaded firearms; they are the most deadly and unerring things that have ever been created by man. You don't have to take any pains at all with them; you don't have to have a rest, you don't have to have any sights on the gun, you don't have to take aim, even. No, you just pick out a relative and bang away, and you are sure to get him. A youth who can't hit a cathedral at thirty yards with a Gatling gun in three-quarters of an hour, can take up an old empty musket and bag his grandmother every time, at a hundred. Think what Waterloo would have been if one of the armies had been boys armed with old muskets supposed not to be loaded, and the other army had been composed of their female relations. The very thought of it makes one shudder.

There are many sorts of books; but good ones are the sort for the young to read. Remember that. They are a great, an inestimable, and unspeakable means of improvement. Therefore be careful in your selection, my young friends; be very careful; confine yourselves exclusively to Robertson's Sermons, Baxter's *Saint's Rest, The Innocents Abroad,* and works of that kind.

But I have said enough. I hope you will treasure up the instructions which I have given you, and make them a guide to your feet and a light to your understanding. Build your character thoughtfully and painstaking upon these precepts, and by and by, when you have got it built, you will be surprised and gratified to see how nicely and sharply it resembles everybody else's.

Student Response Booklet

End-of-Year Integrated Assessment

Student Name _____

Date _____

Getting Started

You'll be spending the next several class periods reading and responding to three selections: "If," a poem by the British author Rudyard Kipling; "Polonius's Advice to Laertes" from the play *Hamlet,* by William Shakespeare; and the essay "Advice to Youth," by the American author Mark Twain. Read these selections with a critical eye, making connections between what you know of your world and what you think the writers were saying about their world at the time they wrote. These selections are printed in the Reader; the blank column beside the text is for you to take notes in as you read.

This booklet provides a variety of opportunities to react to the selections. At different times, you may be working alone, with a partner, or with a small group of classmates. There is space in this booklet to respond to questions and to record your thoughts. All of your writing should be done either in the booklet, in the Reader, or on paper provided by your teacher. In evaluating your responses, your teacher will look at all of your writing, so please respond as completely and as honestly as you can.

In evaluating your reading, your teacher will look at how well you

- connect ideas in one selection to those in another selection

- connect ideas in selections to your own experiences

- build an interpretation of a selection by thinking about it on your own and by learning from other students

- understand the major themes of the selections

In evaluating your writing, your teacher will look at how well you

- state your main ideas

- give details and examples to support your ideas

- organize your thoughts

- correct errors you make in grammar, usage, spelling, and punctuation

In evaluating your speaking and listening, your teacher will look at how well you

- contribute to group discussion

- listen to others

- stay on task during group activities

- cooperate with other group members

Section One

1A. BEFORE YOU READ

People often give each other advice about how to behave in certain situations. What advice would you give to a new student at your school? In the space below, freewrite for five minutes, summarizing your advice.

My advice to a new student:

1B. READING AND RESPONDING

Read the poem "If" on page 68 of the Reader accompanying this Student Response Booklet. As you read, record your thoughts and reactions in the blank column beside the text. Use the five active reading strategies—**question, connect, predict, clarify,** and **evaluate**—to help frame your responses.

1C. REFLECTING AND RETHINKING

Review the responses you wrote as you read the poem. Complete **both** of the following activities to help you build your understanding of the poem.

Part One Add to the word web begun here, writing down ideas and feelings that came to mind as you read the advice in the poem.

be level-headed

Advice to Readers

Part Two Answer these questions.

1. What do you think Kipling meant by "If you can dream—and not make dreams your master; If you can think—and not make thoughts your aim"? Explain this idea in your own words.

_____

_____

_____

_____

_____

2. Do you agree with the advice that Kipling gives to the young people reading this poem? Explain why or why not.

_____

_____

_____

_____

_____

3. This poem was written for a young male audience. If you wanted to rewrite this poem for a young female audience, would you make any changes? If so, give two examples of those changes. If not, briefly explain why you would not make changes to the poem.

_____

_____

_____

_____

_____

Section Two

2A. READING AND RESPONDING

Read the speech "Polonius's Advice to Laertes" on page 69 of the Reader accompanying this Student Response Booklet. As you read, record your thoughts and reactions in the blank column beside the text.

2B. REFLECTING AND RETHINKING

Review the responses you wrote as you read. What is Polonius advising Laertes to do, and what is he advising Laertes not to do? Within the appropriate circles below, write down actions, attitudes, or characteristics that Polonius seems either to support or advise against.

Up with:

Down with:

2C. SHARING WITH OTHERS

With a small group of classmates, take turns explaining your diagram from the previous activity. Make sure that each person has a chance to speak while the rest of the group listens. Then discuss the following questions in your group. Record the group's answers in the chart below.

Question	Comments
1. What themes, or important ideas, do you see in this speech?	
2. Do you believe Polonius's advice could apply to your life? Why or why not?	
3. What is similar and what is different about the advice given in "If" and in "Polonius's Advice to Laertes"?	

Section Three

3A. READING AND RESPONDING

Read the essay "Advice to Youth" on page 70 of the Reader accompanying this Student Response Booklet. As you read, record your thoughts and reactions in the blank column beside the text.

3B. REFLECTING AND RETHINKING

Review the responses you wrote as you read the essay. Then answer the following questions.

1. How would you describe Twain's tone, or attitude, toward his subject in this essay? How does he express this tone? Why, do you think, does he use this particular tone in this essay?

   _____

   _____

   _____

   _____

2. What do you think Twain means when he writes, "For the history of our race, and each individual's experience, are sown thick with evidence that a truth is not hard to kill and that a lie told well is immortal"?

   _____

   _____

   _____

   _____

3. What is your opinion of Twain's advice in this essay?

   _____

   _____

   _____

4. Is there anything else you'd like to say or ask about the essay?

   _____

   _____

   _____

3C. SHARING WITH OTHERS

This activity is meant to help you make connections among the selections you have just read. Working in a small group, fill in the chart below. Write down what you think each writer or speaker suggests about the five concepts named. If you feel that a writer or speaker does not address a particular concept, leave the corresponding box blank.

Concept	Kipling	Polonius	Twain
appearance			
truth			
personal relationships			
thoughts			
fighting			

Section Four

4A. RESPONDING IN WRITING: FIRST DRAFT

Choose **one** of the following writing options and write a first draft of your response on the paper provided by your teacher.

Writing Prompt Option One   What are your own views about how adults should advise teenagers to behave? In a brief essay, compare and contrast your ideas with the ideas of one or more of the authors you have just read. To stimulate your thinking, review the freewriting you were asked to do before you read the selections. Also review your answers to the questions that asked you to comment on an author's ideas.

In your compare-and-contrast essay, make sure to

- identify the subjects being compared
- establish a clear reason for the comparison
- include both similarities and differences and support them with specific examples and details
- follow a clear organizational pattern
- use transitional words and phrases to make the relationships among ideas clear
- summarize the comparison in the conclusion

Writing Prompt Option Two   Consider what the authors have to say about how the individual should function in society. Do you think their observations apply to your own society—your school, community, or country? In a persuasive essay, argue that one or more of these selections is either relevant or not relevant to the lives of young people in the United States today.

In your persuasive essay, make sure to

- state the issue and your position on it clearly in the introduction
- appeal to the audience you're trying to convince
- support your position with evidence, such as facts and examples
- answer possible objections to your position
- show clear reasoning
- conclude with a summary of your position or a call to action

Section Five

5A. REVISING AND EDITING

Option One Exchange papers and booklets with a partner. Then read your partner's paper and fill out the appropriate form from this page or the following page. Have your partner do the same for you. Afterward, discuss your responses.

Option Two Edit your own paper by imagining yourself as a fresh reader and filling out the appropriate form from this page or the following page.

Evaluation Form: COMPARE-AND-CONTRAST ESSAY

What more do you need to know about my views on how adults should advise teenagers to behave?

_____

_____

_____

Which examples do you find most helpful in illustrating my views?

_____

_____

_____

What differences or similarities between my views and those of the author(s) need to be clarified?

_____

_____

_____

What would make my paper better?

_____

_____

_____

Name of peer reviewer:

Evaluation Form: PERSUASIVE ESSAY

What more do you need to know about how individuals should function in society as presented in the selection(s)?

_____

_____

_____

How could I state my opinion about the selection(s) more clearly?

_____

_____

_____

What is the strongest evidence to support my opinion?

_____

_____

_____

What would make my paper better?

_____

_____

_____

Name of peer reviewer:

5B. FINALIZING AND PROOFREADING YOUR DRAFT

Write the final version of your draft on these last two pages. Before you hand in your booklet to your teacher, proofread your final draft, looking for specific mistakes in grammar, usage, punctuation, and spelling. Mark corrections on these pages. Turn in your first draft along with this booklet.

Answer Key

Unit One, "They're Made Out of Meat"

For the short constructed-response activities in sections A through D, accept any plausible answer or interpretation that is drawn from evidence in the selection. Sample responses are outlined below. Notice the wide range of responses that show varying degrees of comprehension among your students. *Alternative interpretations can sometimes be equally valid.*

If you would like to assign a score for the performance in this reading section of the assessment, consult the scoring guide at the back of this booklet.

A. BEFORE YOU READ
An acceptable response would be a diagram listing common emotions or attitudes at first contact: for example, "fear," "confusion," "superiority," "surprise," "welcome."

B. READING AND RESPONDING
Sample responses include
- a number of short comments, similar to those expressed by students in the reading model on page 8 in the student book
- several elaborated responses that address the two sections of the poem as suggested in the instructions

C. REFLECTING AND RETHINKING
The two activities on this page address different learning styles to elicit an understanding of the identities of the characters in the story.

Option One   *Sample responses* include the following:

1. The characters are advanced, nonhuman beings from outer space who are refusing to contact humans (meat), because they find humans so inferior and distasteful.

2. A thoughtful reaction to the last line: for example,
   - I find the idea of life on other planets intriguing.
   - It wouldn't be lonely, but reassuring to know that intelligent life exists only on earth.
   - People would appreciate one another more and feel greater kinship if they realized the smallness of the earth and the vastness of the universe.

Option Two   Students' sketches should show that they realize that the speakers are nonhuman and the meat is human. Accept any labels for the speakers' attitude toward the meat that can be inferred from the story: for example, contempt, superiority, or amazement.

Additional Comments This is the place for students to express an unsolicited response to the story, which may give you additional insight into their reading performance. Some students may choose not to accept this invitation.

D. SHARING WITH OTHERS

The activities in this section require students to step back from the story to address how it relates to the larger world. From their responses, you should be able to see how well they connect the author's ideas to common human attitudes toward "the other." In addition, the responses will give you important information about how well students can work together and how much they can learn from one another.

1. *Sample responses* for the chart follow.
   • The characters resemble European explorers or settlers encountering native peoples, in that they assume their own kind is superior.
   • The characters resemble the upper-class or middle-class people who worry that the poor are moving into their neighborhoods, in that they feel revulsion toward them and refuse to welcome them.
   • The characters resemble people who resist the idea that animals have intelligence and emotions in that they are amazed at the capabilities of beings unlike themselves.

2. *Sample responses* to the question follow.
   • He wanted people to shift their perspective and see humans as perishable, gross, and not very intelligent.
   • He wanted people to feel a kinship to one another as human beings and perceive differences among themselves as insignificant.
   • He wanted people to consider the idea of intelligent life in space.
   • He wanted people to recognize how they prejudge one another.

E. RESPONDING IN WRITING

Before students begin writing, go over both assignments with them to make sure they understand what is expected. Especially point out the standards in the box after each assignment: these standards can help students structure their responses as well as show them the criteria for scoring their work.

In scoring the written part of this assessment you will be looking for students' ability to construct a coherent eyewitness report or reflective essay within the pressures and constraints of a 30-minute time limit. Use the rubrics on the following page to help you analyze the assignment. Then to assign an overall rating, refer to the 6-point scoring guide at the back of this booklet.

Writing Assessment Form

Option One: EYEWITNESS REPORT

Ideas and Content	Weak	Average	Strong
• Focuses on an event that has personal or historical significance			
• Answers the five *W*'s: *who, what, when, where,* and *why*			
• Creates a sense of immediacy using precise language and sensory images			
• Presents events in a clear, logical order			
• Captures the mood of the event			

Option Two: REFLECTIVE ESSAY

Ideas and Content	Weak	Average	Strong
• Writes in the first person			
• Uses figurative language, dialogue, sensory details, or other techniques to re-create the experience for the reader			
• Explains the significance of the event			
• Makes an observation about life based on the experience			
• Encourages readers to think about the significance of the experience in light of their own lives			

Overall Rating _____

For Both Writing Assignments

Areas to work on in the future: _____

_____

_____

Answer Key

For the short constructed-response activities in sections A through D, accept any plausible answer or interpretation that is drawn from evidence in the selection. Sample responses are outlined below. Notice the wide range of responses that show varying degrees of comprehension among your students. *Alternative interpretations can sometimes be equally valid.*

If you would like to assign a score for the performance in this reading section of the assessment, consult the scoring guide at the back of this booklet.

A. BEFORE YOU READ

An acceptable response would be a cartoon to represent the stereotype of a particular group. For example, the stereotype of a teenaged boy might include the labels "bad acne," "an attitude," "oversized clothes," and "basketball."

B. READING AND RESPONDING

Sample responses include
- a number of short comments, similar to those expressed by students in the reading model on page 8 in the student book
- several elaborated responses that address the three sections of the poem as suggested in the instructions

C. REFLECTING AND RETHINKING

The two activities on this page address different learning styles to elicit a basic understanding of the poem.

Option One *Sample responses* to the questions follow.

1. "You" refers to non-Asians who hold stereotypical views of Asian women; "they" refers to the stereotypes of Asian women— Suzie Wong, Madame Butterfly, and geisha ladies; "we" and "ourselves" refer to real Asian-American women.

2. The stereotypical women at the beginning of the poem are alluring and deferential to men, particularly non-Asian men. They dress in kimonos or cheongsams. They are exotic, silent, with downcast eyes or calculating ways. The real Asian-American women at the end of the poem are unlike these stereotypes. They are "stepping on," without the familiar trappings. They are not exotic or alien. They see themselves and others clearly, are strong, speak their minds, and see their dreams happening.

Option Two *Sample responses* follow.

- **Who Doesn't Live Here:** a drawing of Suzie Wong in a cheongsam or Madame Butterfly or a geisha girl in a kimono, or an evil dragon lady, captioned appropriately. They might have downcast eyes or closed mouths to show their silence.

- **Who Does:** a drawing of one or more powerful Asian-American women, perhaps in Western dress, perhaps triumphant-looking, direct-gazing, or open-mouthed, captioned appropriately.

D. SHARING WITH OTHERS

The questions in this section require students to step back from the poem and evaluate it against their own experiences. From students' responses, you should be able to judge how well they understand the tone and theme of the poem. In addition, the responses will give you important information about how well students can work together and how much they can learn from one another. *Sample responses* to the questions follow.

1. The tone of the poem might be described as defiant, proud, determined, or impatient.

2. A summary of the theme might be that real Asian-American women are not like the silent, exotic, and deferential stereotype but instead are strong and coming into themselves.

3. Acceptable responses would be comparisons of the speaker's reaction to stereotyping with group members' reactions. For example,
   - Her anger is similar to mine when I hear people talk about "fat broads."
   - David says he's more amused and just laughs it off when people expect him to play basketball well just because he's African-American.

E. RESPONDING IN WRITING

Before students begin writing, go over both assignments with them to make sure they understand what is expected. Especially point out the standards in the box after each assignment: these standards can help students structure their responses as well as show them the criteria for scoring their work.

In scoring the written part of this assessment you will be looking for students' ability to construct a coherent persuasive essay or critical review within the pressures and constraints of a 30-minute time limit. Use the rubrics on the following page to help you analyze the assignment. Then to assign an overall rating, refer to the 6-point scoring guide at the back of this booklet.

Writing Assessment Form

Option One: PERSUASIVE ESSAY

Ideas and Content	Weak	Average	Strong
• Clearly states the issue and identifies the student's position in the introduction			
• Appeals to the audience the student is trying to convince			
• Supports position with facts and examples			
• Answers possible objections to the student's position			
• Shows clear reasoning			
• Concludes with a summary of the student's position or a call to action			

Option Two: CRITICAL REVIEW

Ideas and Content	Weak	Average	Strong
• Identifies the work and provides a brief summary			
• States an opinion of the work and makes clear the criteria used to judge it			
• Supports the critique of the work with well-chosen details and examples from the text			
• Organizes arguments and supporting details in a way that is easy to follow			
• Concludes with a recommendation to the reader regarding the work			

Overall Rating _____

For Both Writing Assignments

Areas to work on in the future: _____

_____

Improvements made since the last assessment: _____

_____

Answer Key

For the short constructed-response activities in sections A through D, accept any plausible answer or interpretation that is drawn from evidence in the story. Sample responses are outlined below. Notice the wide range of responses that show varying degrees of comprehension among your students. *Alternative interpretations can sometimes be equally valid.*

If you would like to assign a score for the performance in this reading section of the assessment, consult the scoring guide at the back of this booklet.

A. BEFORE YOU READ
Sample responses include a list of remedies for depression, for example:
- talk to a friend, relative, or member of the clergy
- seek professional therapy
- take antidepressant medication
- get some exercise
- work as a volunteer; helping others may make you feel better about yourself

B. READING AND RESPONDING
Sample responses include
- a number of short comments, similar to those expressed by students in the reading model on page 8 in the student book
- several elaborated responses that address the three sections of the selection as suggested in the instructions

C. REFLECTING AND RETHINKING
The two activities on this page address different learning styles to elicit an understanding of the narrator's actions and feelings over the course of the story.

Option One

1. *Sample responses* include the following:
   - I think going skiing and then spending the night outside in the bitter cold was a weird but effective cure for her depression. Just being out in nature and seeing its beauty gives me perspective when I am sad. She had to make the choice that was right for her, and she did. She didn't want to take medication; she wanted to solve the problem in her own way.
   - In my opinion, risking your life by going camping in below-freezing temperatures is not the best way to cure depression. It seemed to work for the narrator, but maybe if she had begun taking medication, she would have had a better chance for a complete cure; there is no evidence in the story that she has completely cured herself.

2. *Sample responses* include the following:
  • Her adventure challenged her and focused her mind on more basic, meaningful things than her troubles.
  • Her fear and effort at survival made her appreciate life and the simple things like the beginning of a new day so much more.

Option Two Students should be able to express and then summarize the narrator's feelings during the four parts of the story. Possible emotions and sensations are as follows:

1. **Beginning:** depression, sadness, lethargy, heartbreak
2. **Day:** clarity, sharpness, appreciation, chilliness, wonder
3. **Night:** fear, pain, numbness, bitter cold, self-criticism
4. **Morning:** joy, exhilaration, celebration, hope

D. SHARING WITH OTHERS

The activities in this section require students to examine the writer's use of description and to explore the effect of the natural world on the writer. Students will have a chance to discuss their observations and consider other viewpoints.

Part One *Sample answers* for the chart are as follows:
  • **Passage:** "When everything in your life is uncertain . . . my lungs only filled up halfway" (p. 19) **Inner State:** clarity, stillness, expectancy
  • **Passage:** "It was utterly quiet out there . . . I didn't know the words" (p. 20) **Inner State:** uncertainty, intrusion
  • **Passage:** "I wish I could tell you . . . convinced me I must still be alive" (pp. 21–22) **Inner State:** fear, terror
  • **Passage:** "But then the sky began to get gray . . . she said nothing ever tasted so good" (p. 22) **Inner State:** joy, triumph

Part Two *Sample answers* to the question are as follows:
  • The natural world gives the narrator a test of survival and a reminder of what it means to be alive in the most basic sense.
  • The natural world gives her beauty to focus on instead of the responsibilities and disappointments of her everyday life.
  • The natural world gives her the ability to see clearly and to see outside herself.

E. RESPONDING IN WRITING

Before students begin writing, go over both assignments with them to make sure they understand what is expected. Especially point out the standards in the box after each assignment: these standards can help students structure their responses as well as show them the criteria for scoring their work.

  In scoring the written part of this assessment, you will be looking for students' ability to construct a coherent reflective essay or critical review within the pressures and constraints of a 30-minute time limit. Use the rubrics on the following page to help you analyze the assignment. Then to assign an overall rating, refer to the 6-point scoring guide at the back of this booklet.

Writing Assessment Form

Option One: REFLECTIVE ESSAY

Ideas and Content	Weak	Average	Strong
• Writes in the first person			
• Describes an important experience in the student's life or in the life of someone the student admires			
• Uses figurative language, dialogue, sensory details, or other techniques to re-create the experience for the reader			
• Explains the significance of the event			
• Makes an observation about life based on the experience			
• Encourages readers to think about the significance of the experience in light of their own lives			

Option Two: CRITICAL REVIEW

Ideas and Content	Weak	Average	Strong
• Identifies and gives a brief summary of the work			
• States student's opinion of the work and makes clear the criteria used to judge it			
• Supports student's opinion with well-chosen details and examples from the text			
• Organizes arguments and supporting details in a way that is easy to follow			
• Concludes with a recommendation to the reader regarding the work			

Overall Rating _____

For Both Writing Assignments

Areas to work on in the future: _____

_____

_____

Improvements made since the last assessment: _____

_____

_____

Answer Key

For the short, constructed-response activities in sections A through D, accept any plausible answer or interpretation that is drawn from evidence in the selection. Sample responses are outlined below. Notice the wide range of responses that show varying degrees of comprehension among your students. *Alternative interpretations can sometimes be equally valid.*

If you would like to assign a score for the performance in this reading section of the assessment, consult the scoring guide at the back of the booklet.

A. BEFORE YOU READ
Students should express personal reactions to the foreign critic's statement and explain whether they think it is fair or unfair.

B. READING AND RESPONDING
Sample responses include
- a number of short comments, similar to those expressed by students in the reading model on page 8 in the student book
- several elaborated responses that address the two sections of the selection as suggested in the instructions

C. REFLECTING AND RETHINKING
The two activities on this page address different learning styles to elicit an understanding of the author's thoughts, feelings, and ideas.

Option One   *Sample responses* include the following:
- I agree with Mark Twain's definition of a "real" civilization. However, I would add some other elements. For example, I think that in a civilized society there is an emphasis on providing a good education for everyone. In addition, I think a civilized society would provide free medical care for everyone who could not afford it.
- I don't agree with Twain's definition of what constitutes a "real" civilization. I think he created an artificial definition of civilization in order to be humorous and to make a point in his essay about the criticism of America that he considered to be unfair.
- I think that Mark Twain is very proud of America's "invention" of human liberty and how this development affected the world as a whole. Twain is upset or hurt by the English critic's unwillingness to recognize America's contribution to world civilization.

Option Two   Students should be able to work together in pairs to role-play the meeting between Mark Twain and Sir Lepel Griffin. Their role-plays should reflect their understanding of Twain's views and how they differ from those of the English critic. A summary of Twain's feelings about Griffin's opinions of American civilization might include the following:

1. He disagrees with the critic because he believes that, since eliminating slavery, America is the only real civilization in the world.
2. He also believes it was America that encouraged other countries to seek their freedom from oppression.
3. He believes that far from being uncivilized, America invented civilization.

D. SHARING WITH OTHERS

The activities in this section require students to examine the writer's attitude toward his subject and to explore key themes in the selection.

Part One *Sample answers* for the chart are as follows:

Description of Tone: In the first paragraph of the essay, Twain expresses a humorous tone.

Quotation: "And now comes Sir Lepel Griffin, whom I had not suspected of being in the world at all, and says. . . ."

Opinion of Tone: Twain's humorous tone in the first paragraph was a good way of making a reader interested in what he had to say.

Description of Tone: By the end of the essay I think he's feeling outraged that America's contributions to the advance of civilization aren't recognized, although his "outrage" is probably tongue-in-cheek.

Quotation: "Who woke that printing press out of its trance of three hundred years? Let us be permitted to consider that we did it."

Opinion: Twain's feeling of outrage at the end of the essay enabled him to present his conclusions in a forceful way.

Part Two *Sample answers* to the questions are as follows:

1. Mark Twain is referring to America's ending slavery as a result of the Civil War. He believes that once slavery was eliminated from American society, the country became the "one real civilization in the world." This essay was probably written about 30 years after the end of the Civil War.

2. Mark Twain is probably referring to the American Revolution and how it inspired other countries, such as France, to establish democracy as well. The United States became the first country founded as a democracy, based on the rights of the individual; this development inspired people in several other countries to follow the United States's example.

E. RESPONDING IN WRITING

Before students begin writing, go over both assignments with them to make sure they understand what is expected. Especially point out the standards in the box after each assignment. These standards can helps students structure their responses as well as show them the criteria for scoring their work.

In scoring the written part of this assessment, you will be looking for students' ability to construct a coherent literary interpretation or persuasive essay within the pressures and constraints of a 30-minute time limit. Use the rubrics on the following page to help you analyze the assignment. Then to assign an overall rating, refer to the 6-point scoring guide at the back of this booklet.

Writing Assessment Form

Option One: LITERARY INTERPRETATION

Ideas and Content	Weak	Average	Strong
• Clearly identifies the title and author of the literary work			
• Gives a clearly stated interpretation at or near the beginning of the essay			
• Presents evidence and quotations from the text to support the interpretation			
• Takes into account other interpretations and contradictory evidence			

Option Two: PERSUASIVE ESSAY

Ideas and Content	Weak	Average	Strong
• States the issue and his or her position on it clearly in the introduction			
• Writes for the audience he or she is trying to convince			
• Supports position with evidence, such as facts and examples			
• Answers possible objections to his or her position			
• Shows clear reasoning			
• Concludes with a summary of position or a call to action			

Overall Rating _____

For Both Writing Assignments

Areas to work on in the future: _____

_____

Improvements made since the last assessment: _____

_____

Answer Key

Copyright © McDougal Littell Inc.

Unit Five, "Working Girls" and "What Work Is"

For the short constructed-response activities in sections A through D, accept any plausible answer or interpretation that is drawn from evidence in the selections. Sample responses are outlined below. Notice the wide range of responses that show varying degrees of comprehension among your students. *Alternative interpretations can sometimes be equally valid.*

If you would like to assign a score for the performance in this reading section of the assessment, consult the scoring guide at the back of this booklet.

A. BEFORE YOU READ
Sample responses under the heading "My Experience with Work" include a brief description of a work experience, such as "I worked at the supermarket in my neighborhood after school." Under the heading "My Feelings About This Experience," *sample responses* include:
- The work was difficult.
- I enjoyed the people I worked with.
- The job made me feel useful.

B. READING AND RESPONDING
Sample responses include
- a number of short comments, similar to those expressed by students in the reading model on page 8 in the student book
- several elaborated responses that address the two poems as suggested in the instructions

C. REFLECTING AND RETHINKING
The two activities on this page address different learning styles to elicit an understanding of the speakers' thoughts and feelings about work and about key themes in the poems.

Option One

1. *Sample responses* include the following:
   - The younger girls are fresh, hopeful, and inexperienced in comparison to the older women, who understand more about life and have more realistic expectations than the younger workers. The older woman have "wisdom," while the younger workers have "beauty."

2. *Sample responses* include the following:
   - The experience of looking for a job reminds the speaker that his brother works very hard and that the speaker has failed to express his feelings for and appreciation of his brother. The speaker seems to be envious of his brother, as well as loving and admiring of him, but he also feels alienated or separated from him.

Sample responses follow:

- "Working Girls": A picture of the older and younger women on their way to work is appropriate.
- "What Work Is": A picture of the narrator waiting in line outside of the Ford plant is appropriate.

Accept any captions that summarize the main ideas expressed in the pictures.

D. SHARING WITH OTHERS

The activities in this section require students to delve deeper into the selections, to go beyond their individual perspectives, and to consider larger thematic issues. From their responses, you should be able to judge how well they understand the theme of the selections. In addition, the responses will tell you how well students work together and how much they can learn from one another.

Part One *Sample responses* for the chart are as follows:

- "Green and gray streams" refers to the younger and older women workers, who walk side by side to work. The older women don't have the same sense of hope and expectation as the younger women. They have been "over the way" and learned that their innocent optimism is gone ("the end of life's gamble"); now they are tired and resigned to what life has given them.
- In "What Work Is," the speaker is talking about his inability to express his love for his brother. He's been reminded of his feelings for his brother as he stands in line outside the Ford plant looking for work. But, he has difficulties communicating with his brother, or feels alienated from him, because they have had very different experiences in life and have different views of "what work is."

Part Two *Sample responses* to the question are as follows:

- In "Working Girls," the speaker focuses on the sense of expectation and hope of the younger working girls in comparison to the lack of expectation and hope of the older women. The main theme concerns the wisdom and acceptance of life that comes with age. The speaker appreciates or understands the wisdom that has been gained by the older women, but he seems disconnected from their experience and much more interested in the "peach bloom of young years."
- In "What Work Is," the speaker's description of looking for work becomes personalized when the experience reminds him of his unacknowledged love for his brother, who is also victimized by work experiences. The theme of this poem concerns the futility that workers endure in their pursuit of "The American Dream," and the loneliness and alienation of that pursuit.

E. RESPONDING IN WRITING

Before students begin writing, go over both assignments with them to make sure they understand what is expected. Especially point out the standards in the box after each assignment. These standards can help students structure their responses as well as show them the criteria for scoring their work.

In scoring the written part of this assessment, you will be looking for students' ability to construct a coherent comparison-and-contrast essay or eyewitness report within the pressures and constraints of a 30-minute time limit. Use the rubrics on the following page to help you analyze the assignment. Then to assign an overall rating, refer to the 6-point scoring guide at the back of this booklet.

Writing Assessment Form

Option One: COMPARISON-AND-CONTRAST ESSAY

Ideas and Content	Weak	Average	Strong
• Identifies the subjects being compared			
• Establishes a clear reason for the comparison			
• Includes both similarities and differences and supports them with specific examples and details			
• Follows a clear organizational pattern			
• Uses transitional words and phrases to make the relationships among ideas clear			
• Summarizes the comparison in the conclusion			

Option Two: EYEWITNESS REPORT

Ideas and Content	Weak	Average	Strong
• Focuses on the event described in one of the poems			
• Answers the five *W*'s: *who, what, when, where,* and *why*			
• Creates a sense of immediacy using precise language and sensory images			
• Presents events in a clear, logical order			
• Captures the mood of the event			

Overall Rating _____

For Both Writing Assignments

Areas to work on in the future: _____

_____

_____

Improvements made since the last assessment: _____

_____

_____

Answer Key

For the short constructed-response activities in sections A through D, accept any plausible answer or interpretation that is drawn from evidence in the selection. Sample responses are outlined below. Notice the wide range of responses that show varying degrees of comprehension among your students. *Alternative interpretations can sometimes be equally valid.*

If you would like to assign a score for the performance in this reading section of the assessment, consult the scoring guide at the back of this booklet.

A. BEFORE YOU READ
Sample responses include a brief description of how a student uses his or her free time and how he or she feels about free time. Words or phrases that express a student's feeling about free time include
- feel pressured to use it productively
- something I look forward to
- provides a balance in my life

B. READING AND RESPONDING
Sample responses include
- a number of short comments, similar to those expressed by students in the reading model on page 8 in the student book
- several elaborated responses that address the three sections of the selection in as suggested in the instructions

C. REFLECTING AND RETHINKING
The two activities on this page address different learning styles to elicit an understanding of the major themes of the selection and how they were expressed.

Option One

1. *Sample responses* include the following:
- I think the statement means that our "leisure time" isn't really free time at all. We work at having fun. Even when we're supposed to have fun, we keep working in our spare time, or we approach leisure activities with the same goals and attitudes as those we apply to work.

2. *Sample responses* include the following:
- I disagree with the author. My free time is important to me, and I don't allow the pressures of schoolwork to interfere with it.
- I agree with the author. Even when I'm supposed to be having fun, I'm worried about my after-school job and my schoolwork. I can't let myself have fun anymore.

Option Two   Students should be able to role-play a dialogue that shows they understand the main themes of the essay. Possible phrases that sum up their thoughts about leisure time in our society include:

- leisure time isn't valued by our society
- our society places limits on our leisure time
- people are made to feel guilty for enjoying their leisure time

D. SHARING WITH OTHERS

The activities in this section require students to identify the main ideas of the selection. Students will have a chance to discuss their observations and consider other viewpoints.

Part One *Sample responses* follow.

1. Main Idea: We are forced to work too many hours to make a living.

   Supporting Detail: In an age of corporate layoffs, executives work 70+ hours per week to keep their jobs.

2. Main Idea: We feel guilty when we're not working.

   Supporting Detail: The Protestant work ethic makes us think that leisure time is "something bad."

3. Main Idea: Technology binds us ever more closely to our jobs.

   Supporting Detail: With cell phones and faxes, we can't escape from our work.

4. Main Idea: Without work, our lives would seem empty and meaningless.

   Supporting Detail: "The more success we achieve, the stronger our identity."

Part Two

1. *Sample answers* to the question are as follows:

- I think Posner began the essay in this way because he wanted to personalize the subject. Reading about his friend in the first paragraph hooked me into wanting to read the rest of the article.
- I think Posner began the essay in this way to establish the themes he would be discussing in the rest of the selection. After reading this paragraph, I understood what the essay would be about.

2. *Sample answers* to the question are as follows:

- I agree with the author. I think that today we are so intent on succeeding at our leisure-time activities that we don't really enjoy them. Work and leisure become equally competitive.
- I disagree with the author. I think that how we handle our free time is a very personal choice. Many people do enjoy themselves. They use leisure time to have fun. The people who don't are very competitive and overstressed. Their problems have nothing to do with society; they are personal.

E. RESPONDING IN WRITING

Before students begin writing, go over both assignments with them to make sure they understand what is expected. Especially point out the standards in the box after each assignment. These standards can help students structure their responses as well as show them the criteria for scoring their work.

In scoring the written part of this assessment, you will be looking for students' ability to construct a coherent critical review or reflective essay within the pressures and constraints of a 30-minute time limit. Use the rubrics on the following page to help you analyze the assignment. Then to assign an overall rating, refer to the 6-point scoring guide at the back of this booklet.

Writing Assessment Form

Option One: CRITICAL REVIEW

Ideas and Content	Weak	Average	Strong
• Identifies and gives a brief summary of the work			
• States the student's opinion of the work and makes clear the criteria used to judge it			
• Supports the student's opinion with well-chosen details and examples from the text			
• Organizes arguments and supporting details in a way that is easy to follow			
• Concludes with a recommendation to the reader regarding the work			

Option Two: REFLECTIVE ESSAY

Ideas and Content	Weak	Average	Strong
• Is written in the first person			
• Describes an important experience in the student's life			
• Uses figurative language, dialogue, sensory details, or other techniques to re-create the experience for the reader			
• Explains the significance of the event			
• Makes an observation about life based on the experience			
• Encourages readers to think about the significance of the experience in light of their own lives			

Overall Rating _____

For Both Writing Assignments

Areas to work on in the future: _____

_____

Improvements made since the last assessment: _____

_____

Answer Key

Unit Seven, "The Lesson"

For the short constructed-response activities in sections A through D, accept any plausible answer or interpretation that is drawn from evidence in the selection. Sample responses are outlined below. Notice the wide range of responses that show varying degrees of comprehension among your students. *Alternative interpretations can sometimes be equally valid.*

If you would like to assign a score for the performance in this reading section of the assessment, consult the scoring guide at the back of this booklet.

A. BEFORE YOU READ

Acceptable responses include any description of a situation in which the student was picked on by a group for some reason. Some students may choose to express their responses by drawing a picture about the experience.

B. READING AND RESPONDING

Sample responses include

- a number of short comments, similar to those expressed by students in the reading model on page 8 of the student book
- several elaborated responses that address the two sections of the selection as suggested in the instructions

C. REFLECTING AND RETHINKING

The two activities on this page address different learning styles to elicit an understanding of the people and the themes in this selection.

Option One

1. *Sample responses* include the following:
- I think that Seymour was very generous in helping the author. He defended him because he understood how much their taunts had hurt him.
- I was glad that Seymour stuck up for the author. Seymour didn't want the author to suffer the way he had the previous winter.

2. *Sample responses* include the following:
- I think he is referring to the effect their shared poverty had on the boys' lives. Since everyone in the neighborhood was poor, they accepted one another.
- I think the author is saying that there was no prejudice in the neighborhood. Since everyone who lived there was so poor, no one looked down on anyone else.

Option Two   *Sample responses* might include the following:

- I think the boys in the neighborhood continued to make fun of Seymour because their own lives were so hard that they needed to make fun of someone else, or because making fun of someone else was an effective way to deflect criticism from themselves.

- I think the boys in the neighborhood continued their "relentless taunting and mocking" because it made them feel better about their own situations. Also, all the boys were poor and had probably suffered the way Seymour had.

D. SHARING WITH OTHERS

The activities in this section require students to examine the elements of the writer's autobiographical technique and to explore the theme of the selection. Students will have a chance to discuss their opinions and consider other viewpoints.

Part One   *Sample answers* for the chart are as follows:

Event as Anecdote: The author's mother bartered her children's outgrown clothes for other garments she found at the used clothing store in the neighborhood.

Summary of Character, Setting, and Plot: The author's mother and the other mothers in the neighborhood bartered for clothes every year as cold weather approached. The story takes place in a poor, inner-city American neighborhood in 1933, after the repeal of Prohibition.

Purpose of Including Anecdote: The author wanted to entertain and to show how the people learned to cope with their poverty and survive.

Part Two   *Sample answers* to the question are as follows:

- I think the title of the selection sums up the major theme: the author learned a lesson about life from his friend's generosity of spirit. A sentence that sums up this theme is: "I understood that because of his greatness of soul, I had been spared."

- I think the title "The Lesson" refers to the lesson that the author learned from his friend's actions. Seymour helped him out because he knew how much it hurt to have other people make fun of him. A good summary sentence is, "And in that glowing moment, Seymour and I bonded like comrades."

E. RESPONDING IN WRITING

Before students begin writing, go over both assignments with them to make sure they understand what is expected. Especially point out the standards in the box after each assignment. These standards can help students structure their responses as well as show them the criteria for scoring their work.

In scoring the written part of this assessment, you will be looking for students' ability to construct a coherent reflective essay or eyewitness report within the pressures and constraints of a 30-minute time limit. Use the rubrics on the following page to help you analyze the assignment. Then to assign an overall rating, refer to the 6-point scoring guide at the back of this booklet.

Writing Assessment Form

Option One: REFLECTIVE ESSAY

Ideas and Content	Weak	Average	Strong
• Writes in the first person			
• Describes an important experience in the student's life			
• Uses figurative language, dialogue, sensory details, or other techniques to re-create the experience for the reader			
• Explains the significance of the event			
• Makes an observation about life based on the experience			
• Encourages readers to think about the significance of the experience in light of their own lives			

Option Two: EYEWITNESS REPORT

Ideas and Content	Weak	Average	Strong
• Focuses on an event that has personal or historical significance			
• Answers the five *W's*: *who, what, when, where,* and *why*			
• Creates a sense of immediacy using precise language and sensory images			
• Presents events in a clear, logical order			
• Captures the mood of the event			

Overall Rating _____

For Both Writing Assignments

Areas to work on in the future: _____

_____

Improvements made since the last assessment: _____

_____

Answer Key

End-of-Year Integrated Assessment
"If," "Polonius's Advice to Laertes" from *Hamlet,* and "Advice to Youth"

For the short constructed-response activities in Sections One, Two, and Three, accept any plausible answer or interpretation that is drawn from evidence in the selections. Sample responses are outlined below.

If you would like to assign a score for the performance in this reading section of the assessment, consult the scoring guide at the back of this booklet.

SECTION ONE

1A. BEFORE YOU READ
Acceptable responses include
- words and phrases that students associate with helping a new student adapt to the school, such as "following the rules," "getting along," or "making friends."

1B. READING AND RESPONDING
Acceptable responses would be a number of short comments similar to those expressed by students in the reading model on page 8 of the student book.

1C. REFLECTING AND RETHINKING
The two activities in this section help students think about the main ideas or themes of the poem.

Part One An acceptable response would be a word web completed with a number of ideas and feelings that students associate with Kipling's advice, such as: "believe in yourself," "never lie," "don't become a dreamer," and "don't give up after losing."

Part Two *Sample responses* for each question include

1. Kipling thinks that it's important to dream; however, you should be careful not to lose yourself in your dreams. He believes that it's also important to think carefully; however, your thoughts should not be your only goal in life. By implication, he is saying that it's important to act rather than to lose yourself in thought.

2. A positive or negative reaction to Kipling's ideas and support for either response. *Sample responses:*
   - agreement with Kipling's advice because the student might feel that Kipling's positive advice would be an incentive to the readers of the poem
   - disagreement with Kipling's advice because the student might feel it isn't relevant to his or her life

3. A student rewriting this poem for a young, female audience might encourage readers to maintain positive self-esteem and to set high goals for themselves. A student might choose not to rewrite the poem, believing that the text is equally appropriate to either young men or women.

SECTION TWO

2A. READING AND RESPONDING

Acceptable responses would be a number of short comments, similar to those expressed by students in the reading model on page 8 of the student book.

2B. REFLECTING AND RETHINKING

Sample responses for the diagram include the following:

- Up with: showing an interest in other people, staying true to your good friends, standing up for yourself in a quarrel, dressing well but not extravagantly, being true to yourself
- Down with: expressing your thoughts freely, acting impulsively, being overly friendly, quarreling, giving your opinion to everyone, borrowing or lending money

2C. SHARING WITH OTHERS

The questions in this section require students to step back from the speech to address larger, thematic issues and to make connections between "Polonius's Advice to Laertes" and "If." In addition, the responses will give you important information about how well students can work together and how much they can learn from one another. *Sample responses* include

1. Students might allude to the following themes:
   - take great care to keep your thoughts to yourself
   - try to avoid quarrels; however, take a strong stand if you do become involved in a quarrel
   - dress well but not in a gaudy way
   - stay true to yourself

2. An opinion about whether Polonius's advice would be applicable to someone living today. *Sample responses:*
   - Yes, because young people often act impulsively, and he urges them to think about their actions carefully.
   - No, because many young people today are concerned about social and environmental problems, and his advice pertains only to a person's self-interest.

3. *Sample responses* may include the following:
   - Both selections give advice to a young person on how to behave in society. Both selections stress the importance of being true to yourself, and both recommend being friendly to others but not too familiar.
   - The two selections are also different in several ways. "If" offers advice that is meant to help the young listener mature into a productive member of society (stay level-headed; work hard; don't give up; don't worry too much about occasional losses). However, the advice given by Polonius reflects a self-interest and concern for personal appearance (keeping friends; dressing in fancy clothes). Laertes is being counseled to take care of himself first and foremost.

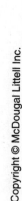

3A. READING AND RESPONDING

Acceptable responses would be a number of short comments similar to those expressed by students in the reading model on page 8 of the student book.

3B. REFLECTING AND RETHINKING

Sample responses for each question include the following:

1. An opinion about the tone of the essay. *Sample response:*
   - I think Twain uses a humorous tone throughout the essay. Examples of his humor can be found throughout the selection. For example, "Always obey your parents, when they are present" and "Be respectful to your superiors, if you have any." I think he uses humor in the essay to make fun of people who give advice to young people and to make fun of the kinds of advice generally given to young people.

2. Interpretations of the excerpt. *Sample response*:
   - I think that Twain is saying that truth is often destroyed while lies are believed.
   - It's easy to destroy or "kill" the truth; however, if a lie is said with enough conviction it is readily believed. He is criticizing the standards of our society, and perhaps the gullibility of people in general.

3. An opinion based on the essay. *Sample response:*
   - Because Twain presents his advice in a humorous way, I think it can't be taken seriously.
   - Although Twain uses humor to describe the advice he gives to young people, I think he is really being subtle about his criticism of the kinds of advice generally offered to teenagers, saying that it is impossible to advise anyone how to behave. He is also criticizing the accepted social values of his time.

4. Students can express an unsolicited response, if they choose.

3C. SHARING WITH OTHERS

The questions in this section require students to make connections among the three selections. From their responses you should be able to judge how well they understand the themes the writers are communicating. *Sample responses* include:

Appearance: Shakespeare suggests that it's important to dress well in order to make a good impression, since your clothes make a statement about who you are. Kipling and Twain do not comment on appearance.

Truth: Kipling believes that people must be prepared to hear their truthful statements distorted by others. Twain believes that the idea that truth is great and will last is incorrect; he thinks that the truth is easily destroyed and a well-told lie believed. Shakespeare only comments on being true to yourself.

Personal relationships: Kipling suggests that his listeners should recognize the worth of all people but not value one person above the other. Shakespeare says that good friends are to be highly valued; however, casual acquaintances, who have not proved their friendship, should not be courted. Twain takes a more humorous view that undercuts the importance of being respectful to superiors or obeying your parents.

Thoughts: Kipling believes that while it's important to think about things and events, it's important not to "make thoughts your aim"; that is, don't lose yourself in your thoughts instead of taking action. Shakespeare suggests that it's important to keep your thoughts to yourself and not to act on any ill-advised thought.

Fighting: Shakespeare urges his listeners to avoid quarrels whenever possible; however, if you are involved in a quarrel, be strong. Twain believes that young people should avoid violence and "leave dynamite to the low and unrefined." Kipling implies that one should be above fighting ("neither foes nor loving friends can hurt you").

SECTION FOUR

4A. RESPONDING IN WRITING: FIRST DRAFT

Before students begin writing, go over both assignments with them to make sure they understand what is expected. Especially point out the standards in the box after each assignment to help them structure their responses as well as show them the criteria by which their writing will be judged.

You will be looking at students' first drafts only as they relate to improvements in their final drafts.

SECTION FIVE

5A. REVISING AND EDITING

You can choose to do this activity with pairs of students or by having students revise their own papers. In either case, the evaluation forms reinforce the standards given to students along with the writing assignments.

Look over the evaluation forms to see whether students have participated in the editing process. These forms, like students' first drafts, are useful in relation to their final drafts. Check to see whether students have made the changes suggested on their forms.

5B. FINALIZING AND PROOFREADING YOUR DRAFT

Use the rubrics on the next two pages to help you analyze students' final drafts. Then, to assign an overall rating, refer to the 6-point scoring guide at the back of this booklet. Keep in mind that students are asked to mark corrections in grammar, punctuation, or spelling on their final drafts, so encourage students to scratch out corrected words and use proofreading marks. Count only students' uncorrected errors.

Writing Assessment Form

Option One: COMPARE-AND-CONTRAST ESSAY

Ideas and Content	Weak	Average	Strong
• Identifies the subjects being compared			
• Establishes a clear reason for the comparison			
• Includes both similarities and differences and supports them with specific examples and details			
Structure and Form			
• Follows a clear organizational pattern			
• Uses transitional words and phrases to make the relationships among ideas clear			
• Summarizes the comparison in the conclusion			
Grammar, Usage, and Mechanics			
• Contains no more than two or three unmarked minor errors in grammar, punctuation, and spelling			

Overall Rating _____

The final draft shows improvement over the first draft in this way: _____

_____

_____

_____

A specific improvement over past assessments: _____

_____

_____

_____

Writing Assessment Form

Option Two: PERSUASIVE ESSAY

Ideas and Content	Weak	Average	Strong
• States the issue and student's position on it clearly in the introduction			
• Appeals to the audience student is trying to convince			
• Supports student's position with evidence, such as facts and examples			
• Answers possible objections to student's position			
Structure and Form			
• Shows clear reasoning			
• Concludes with a summary of student's position or a call to action			
Grammar, Usage, and Mechanics			
• Contains no more than two or three unmarked minor errors in grammar, punctuation, and spelling			

Overall Rating _____

The final draft shows improvement over the first draft in this way: _____

_____

_____

_____

A specific improvement over past assessments: _____

_____

_____

_____

Scoring Guide for Reading Assessment

The following 6-point scale shows the kinds of thinking readers can exhibit in the process of making sense of a selection. Do not expect your students to exhibit all of these behaviors during each assessment. However, the more accomplished readers will show greater depth of understanding and interpretation.

In using this holistic scoring guide, look at a student's performance as a whole and make no judgments until you've reached the end of the assessment.

Exceptional — 6 points

An insightful and thorough interpretation

- Readers at this level demonstrate a sophisticated, thorough, accurate, and deep understanding of the parts of a selection and of how those parts work together as a whole. They show an understanding of nuances and complexities. They draw inferences from subtle cues and plausibly fill in gaps in a narrative. They differentiate between literal and figurative meanings. They attend to and explore ambiguities and contradictions.

- They make connections to their own experience and to other works and ideas. They use the text to generate, validate, and otherwise reflect on their ideas.

- They explore multiple interpretations and may also revise an earlier interpretation when they reread or participate in group discussion.

- They interact with a selection by questioning, disagreeing, agreeing, criticizing, or speculating about ideas and/or text features. They test the validity of arguments through logical analysis and by evaluating the quality and source of evidence.

Perceptive — 5 points

A perceptive and thorough interpretation

- Readers at this level demonstrate a thorough, accurate, and deep understanding of the parts of a selection and of how those parts work together as a whole. These readers, however, may lack the sophistication and impressive depth of exceptional readers. They show an awareness of nuances and complexities but do not demonstrate the keen insight and understanding of exceptional readers. They draw inferences from subtle cues and plausibly fill in gaps in a narrative, but their observations may not be as acute as those of exceptional readers. These readers differentiate between literal and figurative meanings. They attend to and explore ambiguities and contradictions.

- They make connections to their own experience and to other works and ideas. However, the connections may be more predictable than those of exceptional readers. They also use the text to generate, validate, and otherwise reflect on their ideas.

- They may explore multiple interpretations and show a willingness to revise an earlier interpretation when they reread or participate in group discussion.

- They interact with a selection by questioning, disagreeing, agreeing, criticizing, or speculating about ideas and/or text features. The issues they choose, though, may not be as deep or as significant as those chosen by exceptional readers. They test the validity of arguments through logical analysis and by evaluating the quality and source of evidence.

Thoughtful   4 points

A thoughtful and plausible interpretation

- Readers at this level exhibit a thoughtful understanding of the selection as a whole. They draw inferences from subtle cues and plausibly fill in gaps in a narrative, but their observations may not be as perceptive as those of exceptional and perceptive readers. They attend to figurative as well as literal meaning. These readers are aware of complexities but may be confused by ambiguities.

- They make connections to their own experience and to other works and ideas. They may use the text to generate, validate, and otherwise reflect on their ideas but with less depth than exceptional or perceptive readers.

- These readers do not often explore multiple interpretations. They tend to accept a single interpretation and rarely revise when they reread or participate in group discussion.

- They sometimes challenge or question the issues raised in the selection. They may agree or disagree without explaining why.

Literal   3 points

A plausible but superficial interpretation

- Readers at this level demonstrate a very basic and literal, though superficial, understanding of the selection as a whole. They show little awareness of complexities and ambiguities. They may not even respond to a portion of the selection.

- They make few, if any, connections to their own experience or to other works and ideas. Any personal connection to a selection remains on a superficial level.

- They do not explore possible meanings and may even ignore difficult parts of a selection. These readers often refuse to revise or deepen their own interpretation.

- They rarely challenge the issues raised in the selection. If they do, their responses are often expressions of personal frustration or low-level inquiries about literal meaning, such as a definition of a word.

Limited   2 points

A partial interpretation

- Readers at this level seem unable to grasp the meaning of a selection as a whole. Although they demonstrate a superficial understanding of individual sentences and parts of a text, they do not produce an interpretation that connects those parts or that addresses more than some of the minor points or details of a selection.

- They seldom make connections to their own experience or to other works and ideas. The connections they do make are usually tangential to the main issues of the selection.

- They rarely ask questions or evaluate what they read. They either ignore or become frustrated by difficult parts of a selection.

Minimal   1 point

A response to a title, word, and/or phrase

- Readers at this level show an understanding of isolated words or phrases but do not connect them to gain any accurate or coherent ideas or information.

- These readers may have associations with some part of the selection or an isolated word or phrase, but they fail to connect with the central ideas or characters.

- They do not demonstrate an engagement with the selection or an attempt to construct a meaning.

Reading performance is not scorable if the assessment is
- left blank
- illegible
- unrelated to the topic
- written in a foreign language

Scoring Guide for Writing Assessment

The following 6-point scale shows the features that tend to appear in a range of student papers representing various levels of accomplishment. The aim of the scale is to guide teachers in the evaluation of student papers according to a set of standards that are similar to those used in large-scale evaluations of student writing all across the country. A single student's paper may not include all the characteristics identified with any one score point, but it can be assigned a score by looking for the description that most nearly matches its features or its dominant impression. Some allowances should be made for minor errors in style, usage, mechanics, and spelling on the unit assessments, since those tests do not provide time for revision.

Level: STRONG

Exceptional — 6 points	Commendable — 5 points
A paper at score point 6 • Has a clear and consistent focus • Has a logical organization • Uses transitions to connect ideas • Supports ideas with details, quotations, examples, and/or other evidence • Exhibits well-formed sentences varying in structure • Exhibits a rich vocabulary, including precise language that is appropriate for the purpose and audience of the paper • Contains almost no errors in usage, mechanics, and spelling	A paper at score point 5 has the same general features of organization and effective elaboration as a 6-point paper, but it represents a somewhat less accomplished performance. It may, for example, • Have an organization that is predictable or unnecessarily mechanical • Lack the depth and logical precision of a 6-point paper in presenting its argument and supporting evidence • Exhibit appropriate sentence variety and vocabulary but without the control and richness of a 6-point paper • Contain a few errors in usage, mechanics, and spelling

Level: AVERAGE

Proficient 4 points	Basic 3 points
A paper at score point 4	A paper at score point 3
• Has a fairly clear focus that may occasionally become obscured	• Has a vague focus and may contain irrelevant details or digressions
• Shows an organizational pattern, but relationships between ideas may sometimes be difficult to understand	• Shows an attempt at organization, but connections between ideas are difficult to understand
• Contains supporting evidence that may lack effect and so only superficially develops ideas	• Lacks important supporting evidence, or the evidence cited does not sufficiently develop ideas
• Has complete and varied sentences most of the time	• Shows little sentence variety
• Contains some errors in usage, mechanics, and spelling but that do not confuse meaning	• Contains several serious errors in usage, mechanics, and spelling that cause distraction and some confusion about meaning

Level: WEAK

Limited 2 points	Minimal 1 point
A paper at score point 2	A paper at score point 1
• Has a topic but does not include any elaboration	• Only minimally addresses the topic and lacks a discernible idea
• Lacks plausible support for ideas	• Has only a few simple sentences
• Shows limited word choice	• Shows minimal word choice
• Contains serious and numerous errors in usage, mechanics, and spelling that lead to confusion about meaning	• May be incoherent and/or have serious errors in almost every sentence

A paper is unable to be scored if it is
- illegible
- unrelated to the topic
- only a rewording of the prompt
- written in a foreign language
- not written at all